Talk Sense
to
Yourself

Development of Self-Management
and Self-Control in
Educational and Clinical Settings

Talk Sense to Yourself

A PROGRAM FOR CHILDREN AND ADOLESCENTS

Jeffrey Wragg

Longman

First published 1989
by The Australian Council for Educational Research Ltd
Radford House, Frederick Street, Hawthorn, Victoria 3122,
Australia
Telephone: (03) 819 1400

First Published in Great Britain 1990
by Longman Industry and Public Service Management,
Longman Group UK Limited,
6th Floor, Westgate House, The High, Harlow, Essex CM20 1YR,
England and Associated Companies throughout the world.
Telephone: Harlow (0279) 442601
Fax: Harlow (0279) 444501 Group 3 & 2

Cover design and illustrations by Kay Stewart

Printed by Bell and Bain Ltd., Glasgow

British Library Cataloguing in Publication Data
Wragg, Jeffrey
Talk Sense to Yourself: a program for children and adolescents
1. Children Behavioural disorders
I. Title
618.9289

ISBN-0-582-07009-0

Contents

Acknowledgements

This book was begun a number of years ago when I was working with conduct disordered children and adolescents. The techniques and approaches employed in the earlier days became the foundation for the program, but its full implementation in schools could not have come about without the enthusiasm and skills of Nerrida Miller and Bob Mackintosh. Nerrida and Bob acted as support adviser consultants to several New South Wales schools and were responsible for building in-school support teams. I am grateful to Bob and Nerrida for their contribution to this book and for their work in schools which demonstrated that the Talk Sense to Yourself approach could be piloted and run successfully across a wider educational setting.

Preface

Behaviour and conduct disordered children comprise between 3 and 5 per cent of the total school population, yet they can put more stress on schools than any other kind of problem. Younger children also present problems to parents, counsellors and schools as the incidence of hyperactivity and attention disorders appears to be increasing.

This book offers teachers, counsellors and psychologists a set of strategies and techniques which have been applied to these problems within educational and clinical settings for several years. Each section focuses on a different yet complementary set of practical approaches and skills which can be used by schools or counsellors to assist target children to achieve greater self-control and self-management.

Section 1 focuses mainly on a description of the problems and analyses the various methods of treating these disorders within an educational setting from a cognitive behavioural point of view.

Section 2 describes the three programs in detail. Each program is examined in relation to its use within a school or individual counselling or clinical setting.

Section 3 contains a practical retraining program to help children and adolescents with behaviour and conduct problems to develop self-control and self-management skills.

The Talk Sense to Yourself program is designed to be used by counsellors or guidance personnel in conjunction with pastoral-welfare teachers in schools as part of a student-welfare approach to helping conduct disordered students to gain control of their behaviour. Counsellors or psychologists will also find this program extremely valuable in working with conduct disordered children in a clinical setting.

Section 4 examines a range of monitoring and cueing devices which can be used within the classroom by all teachers who wish to help individual children to develop greater self-control.

Section 5 tackles the problem of improving on-task behaviour, attention span and concentration in children who are regarded as attention deficit disordered or hyperactive. A special Talk Sense to Yourself program designed to be used either with specific children, groups of children, or even whole classes is explained. This unit again has fairly wide application as it can be used by individual classroom teachers as well as by specialist counsellors in both educational and clinical settings.

1

Disruption in Schools: Options for Change

Introduction to Conduct Disorders

There is no doubt that disruptive students place considerable stress on schools. Walker (1984) comments that children who have been classified as either emotionally disturbed or behaviour disordered appear 'to stress school systems more than any other handicapping condition' (p. 25).

There is some debate regarding the possibility that disruption and serious misbehaviour are increasing. If disruption in schools is viewed from a historic perspective, it is clear that there has never been a 'golden age'. Lawrence, Steed and Young (1984), in their book *Disruptive children — disruptive schools?* summarise the history of disruptive behaviour in schools from medieval times to the early twentieth century and describe the similarities between disruption and aggression in the past and the present. They note similarities through history but point out that the dimensions of the problem have fluctuated. They conclude their comparison by making the point that 'there is direct and indirect evidence from many sources to indicate a growth in the quantity and seriousness of disruptive behaviour in the past decade at least' (p. 10).

There are difficulties in measuring the specific degree of disruption as the definition has changed over the past years. The criteria or changes in tolerance levels appear to have altered as society changes. Frude and Gault (1984) quote from a Department of Education inquiry into indiscipline carried out by Comber and Whitfield (1979) in England, in which the authors suggest that 'prescribed standards and expectations' have fallen sharply. Rubel (1977) believes that in the United States of America the behaviour displayed by students and accepted as normal under present conditions would have been considered as quite unacceptable and shocking only twenty years ago. Investigations into disruption, violence and suspension rates in schools in Australia tend to indicate a rise in these problems but prevalence rates are rarely quoted. The Western Australian Department of Education (1985) Ministerial Working Party Report quotes from a study of local school suspensions by Hyde and Robson (1980), who suggest that suspension rates have increased fivefold between 1968 and 1983. This study also supports a British study by Galloway, Ball, Blomfield and Seyd (1982) in identifying approximately 20 per cent of suspensions occurring because of persistent disobedience and refusal to obey instructions. Three to four per cent of suspensions were for actual violence against teachers while the Western Australian Report also indicates that about 17 per cent of suspensions were for threatening behaviour or assaults on other students. The major causes of suspensions are defined as 'interactional incidents' between teachers and students.

Frude and Gault (1984) conclude that the increase in the behaviour and conduct disorders of adolescence and middle childhood is not as serious as the popular press might like to suggest but that 'school disruption and violence is not a myth'. There are 'many pieces of evidence which together imply that there has been a noticeable increase in disruption' (p. 17). Early and middle childhood problems have also not gone unnoticed as problems of hyperactivity, attention deficit disorders and acting-out behaviour continue to be identified in a high proportion of children. These levels of concern are often expressed in a range of educational settings where teachers require assistance and advice in handling and coping with hyperactive and conduct disordered children whose behaviour stresses the school system perhaps more than any other handicapping condition of childhood. These children are often referred to child guidance clinics, where they represent a significant proportion of all referrals to specialist agencies dealing primarily with childhood problems.

There is evidence that children exhibiting aggressive, antisocial and acting-out behaviour are more likely than children with any other category of childhood emotional disorders to continue their maladjusted life style into adult life (Bornstein, Bellack and Hersen, 1980; Kettewell and Kausch, 1983). Research also indicates that aggressive behaviour and conduct disorders are largely stable over time and that children experiencing these problems can usually be identified in the first few years of school, if not earlier (Olweus, 1979). The need for early intervention is clear because children who exhibit disruptive, hyperactive or aggressive behaviour continually disadvantage themselves in relation to their peers. They disrupt the classroom and their own learning process and are thus at risk for subsequent academic failure and early educational drop out (Kennedy, 1982; Meyers and Cohen, 1984). Their behaviour invites criticism, rejection and punishment from both peers and adults and invariably continues to cause problems for themselves and quite often for those in close proximity.

It is clear that within any school some classes are more disruptive than others and some pupils present greater difficulties in management than others. Many of these children can be identified as disruptive, aggressive, immature, lacking in concentration, and difficult to teach from a very early age (Rossiter, 1983). Considerable research identifies the importance of personality characteristics, family circumstances, and genetic factors as predisposing individuals towards behavioural or emotional disturbance and it would be wrong to ignore these factors. It is also important to recognise that there is an interaction between the school environment and the child which should refocus our concept of disruption as the 'joint responsibility of schools and students' (Western Australian Department of Education, 1985, p. 9).

Individual Deficit or Interactional Approach

Traditional explanations regarding the causes of misbehaviour have tended to ignore the context in which the problems occur. They have relied on the notion of individual deficits to the exclusion of mounting evidence which indicates that at the very least the school organisation, processes and practices can influence behaviour for better or for worse (Frude and Gault, 1984; Lawrence, Steed and Young, 1984; Rutter, Maughan, Mortimore and Ouston, 1979). These newer definitions do not dismiss the pervasive influence of individual characteristics on behaviour but attempt to integrate the research which clearly recognises the influence of the school environment on individuals. The Western Australian Department of Education (1985) Ministerial Working Party on Disruptive Behaviour in Schools concludes that 'contemporary conditions do not deny that children can be naughty or that some children have a greater propensity for "getting under the teacher's skin" than do others'. But what they emphasise is a 'broadening of the responsibility for disruptive behaviour' (p. 8).

Past and current approaches to dealing with disruptive students have tended to focus on the traditional stand-bys of punishment and removal. Schools need to address a whole range of issues which have a bearing on disruption and these will include:

- discipline policies/sanctions;
- curriculum changes and developments;
- organisational and systems approaches;
- skills development for teachers — examining classroom management, conflict resolution, interpersonal skills, etc.;
- pastoral helping approaches for student retraining.

The 'law and order' approach for most schools involves the development of a series of sanctions, rules and surveillance procedures, but as Gai Hawkins (1982) comments: 'Implicit in these approaches is the tendency towards containing the symptoms of disorder rather than investigating it' (p. 13). The focus of the problem is also clearly identified as located 'in the heads of the offenders'.

Another well-tried approach is to remove the offending children to some form of special unit. In the United Kingdom substantial numbers of off-site units have been established. In the United States out of school suspensions and off-site units appear to be used, with the emphasis upon integration into a 'least restrictive environment'. Bradshaw (1987) comments that in the United States 'students with severe behaviour disorders are among the first to be referred out of less restrictive classes and among the last to be socially integrated back into them'. There are many criticisms of off-site units or even special classes located within the school:

- They presume that the problem is caused by the deficits or inadequacies of the student.
- Removal to an off-site unit or a special class takes the pressure off schools to develop better conflict resolution skills, organisational, curriculum and systems changes, etc.
- The focus is clearly fixed on 'experts' or 'others' to fix the child who has been removed because the ownership of the problem has been transferred.
- Reintegration of the offenders at some subsequent date can be quite difficult as the home school often does not want the child back.

There are many more arguments both for and against the use of withdrawal units. However, the points outlined above emphasise the difficulties regarding treatment options. Walker (1984) comments that the 'history of school responses to child deviance and behaviour disorders has been characterised primarily by punishment, exclusion, containment and isolation'.

Most systems have adopted a wide range of approaches and methods for coping with disruption and it is important to integrate many of the options outlined into a comprehensive and multifaceted approach. At the heart of any philosophy regarding the development of systems to deal effectively with disorder in schools is the need to regard the school as the 'centre piece for practical action'. Rutter et al. (1979) actually conclude their analysis of twelve London comprehensives by stating that there was probably a greater effect of schools on children than of children on schools. Obviously, many characteristics of the school can influence the possibility of disruption. Frude and Gault (1984) conclude that any 'comprehensive analysis must consider factors relating to particular incidents, to personalities of individual pupils and teachers, to interaction and social structure within the classroom, to factors in school organisation and ethos' (p. 40).

Policy makers need to recognise that no single approach can solve all problems. The causes of conduct and behaviour disorders are complex and a simple solution will not work. The diversity of problem behaviours and causes requires a multitude of services and systems approaches. It is clear that individual deficits or personality problems are likely to predispose an individual towards conduct disorders but it is equally clear that the school environment can either minimise or exacerbate the situation. At the centre of any model focusing on disruptive behaviour there must be a distinct understanding of the interactional aspects of schools and students.

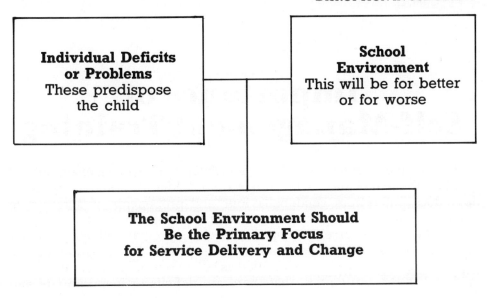

Figure 1   **Interaction of School and Student**

Disruptive behaviour occurs across a wide range of situations and the nature of disruption may vary from mild to severe. It must be emphasised that as the severity of behaviour and conduct disorders increases, a range of options needs to be examined. If behaviour is viewed along a continuum affected by severity, frequency and duration, there comes a point at the very end of the continuum where special treatment options outside the school may have to be considered (Figure 2).

NORMAL MISBEHAVIOUR	CONDUCT DISORDERS	EXTREME EMOTIONALLY DISTURBED
	Frequency Severity Duration	Determine Position on Continuum

Figure 2   **Behaviour Continuum**

Importance of
Self-Management Training

It is naive to expect that merely to identify and punish misbehaviour will produce the real changes which are required. Identification of misbehaviour does not retrain good behaviour and proponents of a return to harsher penalties and punishments need to recognise this fact.

Talk Sense to Yourself is a special teaching program which addresses the issue of conduct disorders and attention deficits. The program focuses on students who have been identified as behaviour or conduct disordered and makes the assumption that there are deficits or inappropriate and maladaptive behaviours which require help and retraining. The program does not assume that misbehaviour is entirely the child's fault and that retraining or helping to correct a set of attentional or self-control deficits eliminates the need for other interventions. Disruptive behaviour should be viewed within the framework of an interactional approach which recognises the school's contribution in reducing or exacerbating these problems.

The focus of this book is on the development of a teaching program which offers to provide adaptive and positive skills for students who are constantly in trouble at school. In choosing to focus on this one aspect of changing disruptive behaviour via the Talk Sense to Yourself program it is assumed that schools will also take the responsibility of addressing many of the other issues which have a direct and significant bearing upon the problems of disruptive behaviour in schools.

Importance of Self-Control Skills

The significance of self-control skills in relation to educational issues was highlighted in 1980 by the New South Wales Committee of Enquiry into pupil behaviour and discipline in schools. The Committee's report was entitled *Self-discipline and pastoral care* and it recommended that all schools should review current practices to determine how effective they were in promoting self-discipline and self-control. The Committee regarded 'self-discipline' as 'one of the prime aims of education' and believed that self-discipline underlies the more academic or intellectual aims of education. The Committee stated that 'self-discipline is essential to achieve these aims and we stress its importance as an indispensable and basic aim' (p. 20).

In order to promote the aim of developing self-control and self-management skills, it is important to identify the essential processes and issues that underpin the conduct and impulse-control disorders. There is clearly a need for early intervention and for the development of programs which focus on self-control and adaptive self-management. It is also important that an underlying philosophy or framework is defined so that a clearer understanding of the aims of a self-management program can develop.

Cognitive Behavioural View of Disruptive Behaviour

Dodge (1985), in an article entitled 'Attributional Bias in Aggressive Children', argues that the perceptions or attributions made by a child about his or her peers play a critical role in the establishment and maintenance of hostile relationships. The aggressive child or adolescent selectively attends to certain cues in the environment and interprets them as confirmatory to the belief that his or her peers are hostile and threatening. This tendency towards making aggressive attributions will lead the child to respond aggressively to peers and they in turn may grow to dislike the child for its behaviour. A pattern of aggressive behaviour is thus established and the consequence for the aggressive and subsequently rejected child is that it develops ongoing behaviour problems. The tendency to 'misattribute' social stimuli as aggressive or hostile has been found to differ significantly between aggressive boys and normal boys or even non-aggressive emotionally disturbed boys. Nashby, Hayden and DePaulo (1980) found that aggressive boys more frequently misassessed aggressive stimuli and also more frequently identified non-aggressive events as aggressive. Feshbach (1979) points out that aggressive acting-out children are often deficient in social skills; thus their behaviour may be inappropriate and this in turn exacerbates many situations. Kupersmidt (1983) examined the relocation of socially rejected children in order to determine the nature of effects between the environment and the individual. It was found that removing aggressive acting-out children from their environments did not succeed because they replicated their rejected status within a few months of being placed with a group of previously unacquainted and new peers. It is clear therefore that changing the child's external situation, which may indeed be valuable, is not as important as examining and changing the internal beliefs and cognitions which produce maladaptive behaviour.

Changing Beliefs Changes Behaviour

Cognitive influences seem to play a pervasive role in the regulation of behaviour. Human information processing is clearly influenced by the beliefs and cognitive attributions or distortions which establish and maintain dysfunctional behaviour. The individual's perception of reality and beliefs about the world as aggressive or threatening are crucial to the interpretation of situations or events (Novaco, 1978; Bandura, 1973). These opinions regarding the significance of cognitive mediation in human behaviour were aptly described more than 2000 years ago by the philosopher Epictetus: 'Men are not moved by things but the views which they take of them'.

Early researchers such as Vygotsky (1962) and Luria (1961) observed that children's inner speech appeared to have a self-monitoring function. These observations regarding the apparant self-guiding function of inner speech, coupled with the earlier work of Luria and Vygotsky, led to the development of a self-instructional training program to help impulsive children to control their behaviour (Meichenbaum and Goodman, 1971).

If inner speech can be regarded as self-guiding, then it is also clear that the content of this inner speech can be adaptive or maladaptive. Children who say to themselves 'I hate tests, they make me nervous' will self-instruct themselves into anxiety and possible test failure. An adaptive self-statement such as 'tests are O.K. if you work carefully and prepare for them' is considerably more positive and helpful. Children and adolescents may hold maladaptive beliefs and unless these beliefs or self-statements are challenged and changed, their behaviour will reflect the beliefs' dysfunctional nature.

Table 1 Examples of Maladaptive Self-Statements

I hate this class . . .

I won't do maths because it's a hopeless subject

If I don't get my own way I won't do anything

Any kid who calls me a name will get punched out

You can't tell me what to do . . . you're not my dad

I'm hopeless . . . I can't do 'X'

Beliefs listed in Table 1 are obviously not helpful and it is possible to predict that maladaptive behaviours will occur because of these self-statements. In order to change behaviour it is necessary to tackle the belief or self-instruction which is maintaining it.

Cognitive behavioural programs offer valuable and significant features relevant to the development of self-control because they focus on internal changes rather than relying upon some method of external control. In many situations where children are regarded as 'out of control' and needing self-discipline, the usual strategies of punishment or removal are employed and both of these focus on the imposition of external control. Table 2 identifies some important contributions of a cognitive behavioural approach as a portable and internal self-guiding tool which can improve the acquisition of self-management and self-control skills.

Table 2   The Value of Cognitive Behavioural Approaches

They do not rely directly on external rewards or agents but concentrate on internal direction.

They provide coping strategies which permit transfer to other situations.

They focus on the learner as an active agent of change rather than a passive participant.

They permit the creation of clearly defined goals and plans of action.

They allow the learner to evaluate performance and progress against plans or goals.

They may in certain circumstances be regarded as portable coping strategies.

They enhance and promote an awareness of the need for self-control and self-management skills.

The Talk Sense to Yourself program, as the name implies, attempts to teach children to use sensible self-guiding language to bring themselves under control. The major aims of the program are to teach both cognitive self-instructional skills and behaviour rehearsal so that target children or adolescents can develop more adaptive levels of functioning and social behaviour.

Applying Cognitive Behavioural Training to Other Problems

In addition to focusing on children with behaviour and conduct disorders, cognitive behavioural approaches can be successfully applied to a second group of children whose poor attention span, lack of concentration, impulsiveness and unrestrained behaviour cause serious problems to themselves and their peers. These children are often referred to as 'hyperactive' or attention deficit disordered and they are usually identified at an earlier age than the behaviour and conduct disordered group. It is worth noting, however, that a significant number of the children identified at this early age may in late primary or early high school also be identified as conduct disordered.

The Talk Sense to Yourself program is directed at attention deficit disorders and hyperactivity. The problems of inattentiveness, disorganised behaviour and distractibility are examined in Section 5, where a special cognitive behavioural training program focuses on developing and retraining self-directed purposeful behaviour.

Nature of Attention Deficit Disorders and Hyperactivity

Every teacher has probably seen children who have problems of distractibility, impulsiveness, short attention span, and hyperactivity. Frequently these children fail to listen to instructions and thus are not ready to start their work, and once started they often fail to complete the work because their attention shifts rapidly from one activity or idea to another. They find it difficult to concentrate and to organise themselves; they call out in class or find it hard to remain seated. They usually have to be closely supervised and because of their inability to stick to tasks or to stay in their seats they frequently become disliked by others and experience an increasing number of confrontations and negative comments from both peers and teachers.

Until recently various diagnostic labels were applied to children with these kinds of problems and they were often referred to as children with minimal brain dysfunction, or as hyperactive or hyperkinetic. The current understanding of hyperactive and learning disabled problems is related primarily to the underlying processes involved in attention and attention deficits. These problems are now referred to as the attention deficit disorders and children may be identified primarily as having an attention disorder with hyperactivity (ADD-H) or an attention disorder without hyperactivity (ADD).

A significant feature of the attention deficit disorders are the complications often associated with the problem and these include school failure, academic difficulties, poor peer relations, and conduct disorders (Safer and Allen, 1976; American Psychiatric Association, 1980). By any measure ADD is a common disorder which can have pervasive and far-reaching effects on the lives of the children and adolescents affected. There is considerable overlap between children experiencing attention disorders and children who are labelled as learning disabled and clearly one of the consequences of hyperactivity and a deficit in attention is the occurrence of significant academic problems.

The characteristics of learning disabled children and children with attention deficit disorders are particularly significant when viewed in relation to 'on-task' or academically engaged time. Academic learning time or engaged time refers essentially to the time students spend actively engaged in an academic learning task (Lomax and Cooley, 1979; Ysseldyke and Algozzine 1983). There are, according to Rieth, Polsgrove and Semmel (1981), two components of academic learning time. The first refers to the specified allocation time scheduled within a school or educational district. There is a clear positive relationship between allocation time and subsequent gains in academic achievement. A major problem with regard to time schedules for instruction is that students may be off task and waste this time in other activities, and thus the second component of academic learning time refers to the actual time during which a student is engaged on learning tasks.

There is a significant negative correlation between off-task variables and reading gains and a corresponding positive relationship between on-task behaviour and reading levels (Stallings, Needels and Staybrook, 1979). A study by Rosenshine (1980) on academically engaged time with Grade 2 and Grade 5 students reported a level of approximately 40 per cent of engagement during a class period. There would clearly be enormous variations in the time spent on task by different pupils and Ysseldyke and Algozzine (1983) investigated this aspect further.

Out of a total school day of 390 minutes they identified approximately 180 minutes which were allocated to academic instruction. During this time students spent approximately 110 minutes in passive responding tasks such as listening to the teacher or waiting for something to happen. Forty-three minutes were spent on active academic responding tasks such as writing (29 minutes), reading (10 minutes), discussing (3 minutes), and reading aloud (1 minute). About another 26 minutes were wasted in inappropriate responding which was mainly comprised of looking around, inappropriate talking, or off-task talking condoned by the teacher.

The purpose of quoting these figures is to focus on the relatively brief time spent by students in actively engaged academic responding. The researchers point out that only 12 per cent of the total school day was spent by students on task-active engaged responding. They also posed the question: 'Is it simplistic to assume that many students do not learn because they are not actively engaged in reading?' (p. 68). These researchers came to the conclusion that there is indeed insufficient academically allocated and academically engaged time spent on learning to read.

This research is even more significant when we examine the plight of children experiencing attention deficit disorders. If average children spend the major part of the academically allocated or scheduled school day on activities other than active academic responding, it is quite logical to assume that children who are distractible, impulsive, and display short attention spans are engaged for even less time.

Importance of Developing On-Task Behaviour

The research on academically engaged time clearly identifies the importance of developing appropriate 'on-task' behaviour. Children who experience attention deficit disorders are obviously more 'at risk' in terms of the percentage of their time engaged on active learning and responding tasks. An increase of eight to ten minutes of appropriate on-task reading behaviour would presumably represent a 50 to 100 per cent improvement on previous levels of engaged reading time. Although it would not be possible to predict a corresponding percentage increase in reading achievement, it is quite likely that significant gains would be made.

Thus a fairly strong argument for on-task training could be developed, but the question remains of precisely what form such training should take. It could also be argued that not only should a high priority be given to some form of on-task training with students exhibiting attention deficit disorders, but that normal children could also benefit from a program which offers to increase academically engaged time.

Torgensen and Goldman (1977) point out that the concept of attention can be viewed in two major ways. The first refers to attention as an internal capacity or faculty, while the second sees it as an information-processing activity. In the latter conceptualisation a failure to recall information is regarded as a failure to apply appropriate strategies or schema for processing information. Torgensen (1977) and Torgensen and Goldman (1977) examined delayed recall and during the delay period the subjects were closely positioned in order to identify lip movements and whispered self-talk. Torgensen and Goldman (1977) noted that learning disabled children 'both recalled less and rehearsed less than normal children' (p. 54). When the learning disabled children could be induced to rehearse they recalled as well as normal children. This finding implies that performance in certain tasks is related to the ability of subjects to employ efficient study behaviours which organise the task rather than regarding memory or some other internal factor as the primary cause.

Students Need to Develop Self-Instructional Skills

Recent research points towards the use of cognitive behavioural approaches as beneficial in promoting improved on-task behaviours and more efficient learning. According to Harris (1986), research has provided support for the hypothesis that poor performance among learning disabled children is frequently the result of problems in self-regulation and organised strategic behaviours rather than an inability to acquire and execute specific strategies. The cognitive behavioural approaches focus mainly on teaching students to develop a series of self-instructional plans or schema to direct their actions.

Vygotsky (1962) believed that children's self-verbalisations were purposeful and that as the child grew towards adolescence overt vocalisations were replaced by a more mature and well-developed self-regulatory inner language.

Luria (1961) instructed children on what to say in order to direct their motor activity; he then observed the influence of their inner speech on behaviour.

Inner Speech Can Direct and Organise Behaviour

Copeland (1983) comments that the prediction regarding private speech becoming increasingly internalised as the child matures is not well supported by theory and data. Kohlberg, Yaeger and Hjertholm (1968) proposed a five-step model regarding the content of children's private speech whereas Vygotsky had earlier proposed a three-step model. Both models focus on the inward directedness or self-guiding properties of private speech and both indicate a developmental progression moving from audible word play and mutterings towards more 'internalised' whispering and talking and then finally proceeding to silent inner speech or thought.

Meichenbaum and Goodman (1971) drew closely upon the work of cognitive developmental psychologists in devising a self-regulatory verbal self-instruction training program for impulsive children. In this program the child learns to ask certain task-relevant questions such as 'What's my problem?', 'What's my plan?' when confronted with a problem-solving situation. Table 3 shows the five stages involved in this training approach.

Table 3   The Training Stages Used by Meichenbaum and Goodman

---

1 An adult first models the required task while verbalising the instructions aloud.

2 The child performs the task while the trainer instructs the child.

3 The child performs the task while self-instructing aloud and the trainer may give additional prompts, feedback and reinforcements if necessary.

4 The child performs the required task while talking to itself (faded, overt self-guidance — whispered).

5 The child performs the task while guiding performance with covert self-instruction.

The initial results from these self-instructional studies have been encouraging although some studies reported problems with later generalisation across response modes and settings (Meichenbaum and Asarnow, 1979). Self-instructional training has been applied with some success in a variety of other settings and researchers tend to support the notion that private speech can perform a self-guiding and self-regulatory function which has been positively related to on-task behaviour and persistence (Harris, 1986); reduction of impulsiveness (Palkes, Stewart and Freedman, 1972; Urbain and Kendall, 1980); academic achievement (Meichenbaum and Asarnow, 1979); problem solving (Spivack and Shure, 1974); and hyperactivity (Kendall and Finch, 1978).

One study in particular deserves special mention. The authors, Camp, Blom, Herbert and Van Doorninck (1976), combined many of the treatment approaches of earlier researchers in developing a training program called Think Aloud. Aggressive Grade 2 boys were taught to use a four-stage plan which asked them to identify the problem; to analyse the situation and decide how to proceed; to keep to their plan; and, finally, to evaluate their performance. The thirteen-lesson program progressed from cognitive to interpersonal tasks and provided successful training in self-instructional skills. The results of this program by a variety of measures were good and these results generalised to the classroom.

Treatment and Management Approaches

In the past, impulsive disorders have been treated with a range of intervention strategies such as drug treatment, counselling, family therapy, aversive methods, investigation of food colourings, hypoglycaemia, and diet.

Diet

Golden (1984), in his article on controversial therapies, comments that the Feingold diet has been significantly overvalued by subscribers to the approach. Other researchers reach the general conclusion that a very small subset of hyperactive children appears to be influenced by one or more artificial dietary additives (Harner and Foiles, 1980; Weiss, Williams and Margen, 1980).

Medication

Stimulant medication is most often the treatment prescribed for children with these disorders. There is some cause for concern regarding dose-related effectiveness and side effects. Sprague and Sleator (1977) pointed out that a moderate dose of methylphenidate (0.3mg/kg) appeared to be suitable for academic progress but that a much higher dose (1.0mg/kg) was needed before teacher reports which indicated improved social adjustment were obtained. The implication from this study is that dosages which are perceived by significant adults to be appropriate for behaviour and social control are deleterious to academic progress.

In comparison with studies examining physical effects, the undesirable side effects on psychosocial functioning and self-perception have not been as well documented (Whalen and Henker, 1980). Taking pills may alter the self-perception of the child and result in a lessened sense of control and responsibility over situations. Whalen and Henker point out in a later article (1984) that the child on medication may regard itself as different from others and this view is often reinforced by family and teachers. Transgressions by hyperactive children are met with comments such as 'Johnny, did you take your medication this morning?'. Children who are not on medication are usually given clear directives regarding their behaviour. As Whalen and Henker (1984) state, non-medicated children are expected to 'exert some self-control — rather than enlist an external corrective agent in the form of medication' (p. 412).

Cognitive Behavioural Approaches to Developing Internal Control

In the past, medication has all too often been invested with 'control and retraining' properties and therapists, parents and teachers have not implemented further retraining. Pills do not 'fix' or 'retrain' the ADD-H child. They are only agents which can help to reduce levels of impulsive behaviour and provide a more conducive environment in which specific cognitive and skills-based retraining can take place. Meichenbaum (1977) notes that 'the self-instructional training approach was designed to deal directly and explicitly with the self-regulatory defect' (p. 34). Many children with conduct or impulse disorders come from homes where they have not been under adult control, and they have not had the opportunity of observing and internalising a language of self-control, calmness and logic. It is important to redress this situation and to teach these children to think before they act in order purposefully to guide and plan their behaviour.

Cognitive behavioural approaches focus specifically on the child as an agent of change. However, in order to improve generalisation and effectiveness it is important that a clearly structured program be followed so that the target child can master the new skills.

2

Use of
the Programs
in a School
or Clinical
Setting

The material is organised into three separate yet complementary sections. Each section focuses on a set of skills or applications relevant to guidance personnel, counsellors and schools engaged in pastoral-welfare activities where specific attention to behaviour problems and attention deficit disorders is required. The three program units are:

Talk Sense to Yourself for conduct disordered children and adolescents (Section 3)
An individual or small-group program which focuses on the development of self-control and self-management skills for conduct disordered children and adolescents. This program uses cognitive self-instruction and behaviour-rehearsal approaches with target children in a one-to-one or small-group setting. The program has been developed to assist schools, guidance personnel or clinics to train children in more adaptive ways of behaving.

In schools where only small numbers of students reach suspension levels or cause serious concern, this program unit would mainly be used when school counsellors, guidance personnel or teachers with special responsibility for pastoral care (form or year patrons for example) employ it with individuals or small groups of conduct disordered adolescents. In schools where behaviour problems and conduct disordered children and adolescents are present in larger numbers, the program is best used within a team approach; that is, the school selects a team of teachers who will target a number of individuals.

Monitoring and Cueing for behaviour change (Section 4)
This unit concentrates on various monitoring and cueing techniques which can be used in classrooms to promote self-control and self-management skills. It is for use by all teachers trying to help individual students to gain control of impulsive and disruptive behaviour. Monitoring and cueing approaches may be used with children aged between five and fifteen years as a self-management strategy to shape self-control within a classroom setting. This unit is a very useful adjunct to the Talk Sense To Yourself program.

On-Task Training for children with attention deficit disorders and hyperactivity (Section 5)
This unit is intended for use by all teachers who wish to improve the attention span, self-control and academically engaged time of their students. The target group can be individual students, groups or even whole classes which have difficulty in focusing attention and remaining on task. Children aged between five and ten years who have been identified as impulsive, hyperactive or attention deficit disordered are envisaged as the principal targets. The unit has been successfully used in high schools with special classes or mainstream groups experiencing on-task problems.

The programs can be used in both educational and clinical settings.

Application of Programs to Specific Problems

Each of the three units can be used as a separate program but the overall impact of these approaches will be enhanced if they are used in combination with each other.

Table 4 identifies the characteristics of target students and matches the individual with the necessary retraining program. Most students can benefit from being involved in more than one unit but if there is no time or personnel available for supplementary programs, main programs are clearly specified. Many students display more than one of the defining characteristics and therefore a choice may have to be made regarding the program to be employed as the main unit.

Table 4   Matching Student Characteristics with Programs

Student characteristics	Main program unit to be employed	Supplementary program
Reach suspension levels (serious behaviour disorders)	Talk Sense to Yourself	Monitoring and Cueing On-Task Training
Moderate to mild behaviour disorders	Talk Sense to Yourself	Monitoring and Cueing On-Task Training
Impulsive, hyperactive	On-Task Training	Monitoring and Cueing
Attention deficits	On-Task Training	Talk Sense to Yourself
Aggressive, angry	Talk Sense to Yourself	Monitoring and Cueing On-Task Training

Use of Programs within a School Setting

The three programs largely address the issue of individual deficits. They focus on providing teachers and students with specific skills to improve self-management and self-control. In every school there will be a small number of individuals who may require the use of all three programs. Some very poorly controlled children and adolescents have inadequate academic on-task behaviours coupled with high levels of misbehaviour and aggression. Other children in the school may fit more closely into only one of the three programs. Each program, whilst complementary to the others in terms of helping children and adolescents to develop more adaptive levels of functioning and on-task behaviour, is different because of the manner in which the retraining occurs.

Serious misbehaviour may be reduced either in a classroom setting using monitoring and cueing, or within a one-to-one or small-group setting using the Talk Sense to Yourself program. Attention problems may be tackled either within a whole class or a small-group setting. Because the three programs are implemented in different ways, it is necessary to examine each unit in relation to its mode of operation, setting, ethical considerations and prerequisite teacher skills.

Talk Sense to Yourself Program

Aims of the Program

The Talk Sense to Yourself program focuses on the development of self-control and self-management skills which will reduce levels of maladaptive antisocial or aggressive behaviour in children and adolescents (Table 5).

Table 5   Aims and Objectives of the Talk Sense to Yourself Program

Aims:
1 To reduce levels of maladaptive, aggressive and dysfunctional behaviour.
2 To improve or develop
- social and interpersonal skills
- self-management and self-control skills
- appropriate self-instructional inner speech.
3 To develop a set of skills which permit generalisation across situations.

Objectives: (A) Self-Instructional Components
To teach
- self-instructional problem-solving skills
- self-instructional control of impulsive or aggressive behaviour
- self-regulation and self-monitoring skills.

(B) Behavioural Rehearsal Components
To teach
- role rehearsal and role-taking skills
- assertiveness and negotiation skills.
To provide
- adult modelling of both self-talk and behaviour-rehearsal skills.

Setting

The most appropriate setting for a Talk Sense to Yourself program is a one-to-one teaching situation or a very small group. The program can be employed in larger group settings as part of a pastoral-welfare guidance program, but this should only be done if it is anticipated that students will be reasonably well behaved. Where students are out of control and behave badly, it would be more appropriate to use the program in a one-to-one or very-small-group setting.

Who Can Use the Program?

The program should be used by clinical staff or by guidance personnel. It may also be used by teachers who have special responsibility for guidance and pastoral welfare. It is suggested, however, that these teachers consult school guidance personnel and wherever possible work within a Support Adviser program. That is the name given to a school-based system in which 10 to 40 per cent of the staff learn to use the Talk Sense to Yourself program and each member of the team targets a child in order to change its maladaptive behaviour.

Place of the Program within the School Organisation

As the Talk Sense to Yourself program focuses on the development of self-control and the teaching of adaptive self-management skills with students who have conduct disorders, it is necessary for each school to establish the size of the group which requires assistance. If a school has only small numbers of students whose behaviour is causing serious problems which cannot be handled adequately by normal classroom management techniques, the building of an in-school team would not be appropriate. In schools where larger numbers of students cause fairly serious behaviour problems, the Talk Sense to Yourself program should be used by a group of teachers who can act as an in-school support team.

Situation 1 Schools with Few Conduct Disordered Students

In this situation the place of the Talk Sense to Yourself program within the school organisation is low key. The program is usually conducted at a one-to-one or small-group level and therefore school counsellors, guidance personnel and teachers with special responsibility for pastoral care and guidance would work with individuals or small groups. The scheduling of the program units would not usually be organised to fit into the timetable but rather into guidance periods or periods allocated to form or year patrons as part of their special guidance allowance. Counsellors and guidance personnel normally conduct interviews or group work without reference to timetables but where form patrons or year patrons have specially timetabled guidance periods with small groups, it would be possible to conduct the program within such a structure if a particular group required this level of intervention.

Situation 2 Schools with Moderate or Large Numbers of Conduct Disordered Students

The place of the Talk Sense to Yourself program within the school organisation would be more structured in this situation. As most schools do not have sufficient guidance and counselling personnel effectively to retrain larger numbers of misbehaving students, it would be most appropriate to set up an in-school support team. High schools may choose to train between 10 and 40 per cent of the school staff to use this program with target children. In these circumstances all house or form patrons as well as other teachers with special pastoral skills or responsibilities would work with guidance personnel in targeting specific students.

Timetabling of special guidance periods for house and form patrons and other members of the team may be considered. Many schools recognise that teachers spend considerable time after scheduled lessons talking to poorly controlled students and to replace a series of ad hoc discussions with a structured approach such as the Talk Sense to Yourself program will make these sessions more effective without the need for timetabled planning. Where guidance periods or short personal development lessons are built into timetables for those teachers who have special responsibilities for pastoral care, the program can again be incorporated into these periods.

Skills, Responsibilities, and Ethical Considerations for Teachers

It is expected that good interpersonal and pastoral-care skills will be demonstrated by teachers involved in the approach. Before engaging any student in a self-control and self-management program, guidelines on important issues such as informing parents and obtaining assistance and approval from relevant school authorities and guidance staff need to be established.

Teachers who are prepared to assist students to develop greater skills of self-control and self-management in a one-to-one or small-group situation need to recognise that their role changes from a classroom manager to a person who acts as a consultant or helper with the child or adolescent involved in the program. In such a role, certain prerequisite skills are required of the teacher.

Rigid teachers or those who use the power of their position to demand change will not be effective. It is not sufficient merely to talk to or at a student; it is important to listen carefully to the student's comments and also to communicate through eye contact, posture, facial expression and tone of voice that you are interested and concerned. Teachers will need good communication and interpersonal skills which permit them to relate well to students, and demonstrate a capacity to assist students to work on changing maladaptive behaviours.

Many teachers are constantly helping individual students with specific problems and issues and the use of the Talk Sense to Yourself program becomes a structured extension of their pastoral role. However, the more sustained nature of such a program places greater demands upon teachers who are going to be involved with students over a period of time, and where schools build in support teams of teachers to work on retraining maladaptive student behaviour, it is therefore important that counselling or guidance staff be included as co-ordinators and consultants.

Teachers and schools which choose to retrain students with the Talk Sense to Yourself program should not only be aware of the prerequisite skills required but should also ensure that ethical considerations and concerns are identified and discussed with the school executive and counselling or guidance staff.

Ethical Considerations

Teachers should always respect the concerns and responsibilities of parents and guardians and the school should ensure that adequate information is made available at all times.

A voluntary commitment to participation by both student and parents is the only basis on which work with the self-management program can be carried out.

Teachers need to recognise the special position and reponsibilities of trust and influence within a one-to-one teaching situation. They must endeavour to be sensitive and aware of the needs and feelings of the target child.

Teachers should be aware that their capacity to develop a relationship based on concern, support and respect towards the child or adolescent may be crucial in determining the outcome of the program.

Teachers should seek the support and assistance of guidance and counselling staff whenever possible.

Teachers should implement this program as part of a recognised, co-ordinated and evaluated school approach which has the support and backing of the school executive.

School-Wide Approach — Building a Support Team

Where schools consider that the number of students with moderate or serious behaviour problems is sufficiently large to call for a whole-school response, a support-team approach may be considered. Guidance personnel or counsellors may already be working with individuals or small groups of students with the Talk Sense to Yourself program, but the number of students requiring assistance may be so large that specialist counsellors are not able to work with every child. In that situation, a team of teachers can be chosen, selected normally to include form or house patrons and other members of the school staff who either have special responsibilities for pastoral welfare or who are regarded as having personal qualities suitable for inclusion in team training.

Extensive trials of the Talk Sense to Yourself program, using a support-team model, have in fact been carried out in the South Coast region of New South Wales. Four assumptions underpinned the framework of operations:

- It is unrealistic to send students to 'experts' outside the school for quick cures. All schools need to recognise the interactional aspects of disruptive behaviour and provide in-school methods of retraining and assistance.

- Target students have in the main learnt inappropriate behaviour patterns and some retraining and self-management instruction is required.

- Students cannot be expected to learn these skills and implement them in their schools without support and monitoring by teachers. This is needed to ensure generalisation of skills from workshops to class-rooms.

- Teachers need to be helped to learn management skills appropriate to these more difficult and behaviour disordered students.

These premises provide a basis from which specific aims can be formu-lated.

Aims of the Support Team Program

The aims of the program are:
- to identify students whose behaviour and attendance patterns constitute a problem both for themselves and the school;
- to provide special assistance to these target students via a program of self-control and self-management which will enable them to achieve more satisfying and more acceptable levels of behaviour;
- to provide training which will (a) equip an in-school project team with special support and retraining skills, and (b) help all teachers to develop skills in classroom management and conflict resolution.

In the early phases of the New South Wales project, schools were assisted by a special teacher who trained the in-school support team. Staff meet-ings were allocated to the project which was explained to the whole staff and if agreement was reached each school was asked to nominate up to one-third of its staff for training as 'support teachers'. Once the support team was sufficiently versed in the Talk Sense to Yourself program, each member engaged a target student and these children or adolescents began the program.

The remainder of the staff also took part in activities related to class-room management and conflict resolution and therefore all teachers received training. High schools trained between fifteen and thirty-five personnel as support teachers with the aid of the specialist consultant. Once each school had a fully trained and fully operative team the con-sultant withdrew after first nominating two co-ordinators. The school then operated without any further assistance although consultation with the co-ordinators was sometimes necessary.

Following the success of the Talk Sense to Yourself program in this whole-school setting many other schools sought assistance to develop a support team using the program. Several of these schools were in such remote locations that no in-school consultancy service was provided. The Talk Sense to Yourself program together with an explanation of the phi-losophy was sent to the schools and they developed their teams and individual skills by following the program outline. Primary schools also became involved in the project and they too developed small support teams independently. Many teachers in primary schools identified chil-dren in their class with whom they chose to work and used the program outline to teach or retrain individuals, groups, or even whole classes. In each participating school, the conclusions reached regarding the effectiveness of the program were positive.

Most programs could be better developed with the provision of a special consultant and the Talk Sense to Yourself program is no exception. However, there is no doubt that the program can be and has been used without the services of a consultant or special trainer. This has been adequately demonstrated in several schools.

Obtaining Support for and Implementing a School-Wide Program

In order to proceed with the testing of the Talk Sense to Yourself program employing an in-school team, it is necessary fully to inform and consult with teachers and executive staff. The staff should be involved in the decision-making process so that they will feel more committed to the implementation of the program.

Stages in the Development of a Program within a School

The following stages are suggested in the decision-making process and the implementation of the program should then flow directly from the information and discussion steps.

- Establish a need and identify a specific target group of children who could be helped.
- Consider what options the school can examine in order to help students to have a more positive experience. Identify the resources and skills at school and focus on organisation, system, and possible curriculum areas.
- Explore the possibility of adopting a sequenced, planned and organised program such as Talk Sense to Yourself. Initiate discussions with the principal and staff and obtain their support and agreement to train a small support team.
- Approach individuals with skills or experience in guidance and student welfare and select a team of teachers who have good interpersonal and communication skills.
- Become familiar with the program. Ask your school counsellor or member of the guidance team to assist in this training phase.
- Identify target children whose behaviour causes concern.
- Invite the parents of target children to a meeting and explain the nature of the program in helping to develop self-control skills. Obtain their support, and their agreement for engaging the children in the program.

Monitoring and Cueing Program

In the majority of classrooms misbehaving children are reprimanded and admonished for disruptive behaviour. Punishments or threats are often used in order to 'control' the offending child or adolescent. These approaches clearly place the role of correction in the hands of the teacher, who is expected to control misbehaviour by the application of a range of external measures. Because some teachers have charisma, power or status, children do not behave as poorly in their classrooms as in those of a less 'assertive' teacher. If the standard of misbehaviour is solely based on a teacher's performance, the misbehaving child can hardly be said to have acquired self-control; the control is based on the 'ability' of an external agent (the teacher) to produce acceptable behaviour.

Aims of the Program

A monitoring and cueing program attempts to place some of the responsibility for controlling maladaptive and disruptive behaviour on the target child. This program tries to teach a child or adolescent to reflect upon the meaning of a 'cue or signal', and either to inhibit a maladaptive behaviour, or begin an adaptive and previously agreed upon new behaviour.

Setting

Teachers who intend to use one or more of the monitoring and cueing approaches will recognise that the program needs to be set up during 'private time' and implemented in the classroom. Most teachers spend time after lessons talking to misbehaving students in order to reprimand them for their 'out-of-control' behaviour. If a student is causing sufficient disruption in the classroom to warrant a 'private' discussion, this time should be utilised to set up a monitoring or cueing approach. Once clear agreement regarding target behaviours and monitoring signals has been established, the setting changes to the classroom in which the program is to be implemented.

Who Can Use the Program?

The unit is intended for classroom teachers. Many teachers already use a number of non-verbal cues and signals to let students know they are off task or 'doing the wrong thing'. This unit extends what is often a loose and ad hoc approach into a more structured program.

The Age and Nature of Target Children

Students who are poorly controlled and whose behaviour in the class-room causes problems are the likely targets for this program. Children as young as six or seven years of age can be helped to control their behaviour and there is no upper age limit to restrict usage through the senior school. Students who are already being targeted with the Talk Sense to Yourself program can also be linked to a monitoring and cueing unit. However, it is quite customary to use this program on its own with students whose behaviour, whilst causing problems, does not warrant involvement in a more substantial approach.

Additional Considerations

A school-wide approach is normally not required for the implementation of monitoring and cueing programs. However, some co-ordination may be needed in high schools where an in-school support team is working with students on the Talk Sense to Yourself program.

Teachers should discuss the setting up of a program with executive members of staff. This discussion, however, should generally not take up more time than is normal for such situations. Where the behaviour levels of the student involved are more disturbing and give rise to greater con-cern, it would be useful to discuss the proposed monitoring and cueing at greater length with senior staff, and possibly with parents.

On-Task Training Program

Aims

The final program focuses on a cognitive behavioural approach to helping children to gain greater self-control and to improve levels of academically engaged time.

Setting

The program can be used by either guidance personnel or classroom teachers within a one-to-one or small-group setting as well as with an entire class. Teachers or counsellors who intend to use the program with whole classes should first identify children who will require extra training and work with them as a small group before proceeding with the whole class.

Age and Nature of Target Children

The program targets those children who have attention deficit disorders or problems of impulsiveness and hyperactivity. The program can be used with children as young as six or seven years of age and extend into early or middle high school. It can be used with children and adolescents in special or slow-learner classes as well as with children in normal streams.

On-Task Training and Curriculum or Organisational Considerations

Estimates of incidence rates regarding attention deficit disorders range from 5 per cent of the total school population to over 20 per cent in some schools. Where the incidence rate appears to be fairly high, the implementation of a significant program within the school would be of value. Where attention deficit disorders are present in more modest proportions, the program would best be initiated within a small group.

If schools propose to implement the program with a large number of children or classes, there will be organisational considerations. Members of staff should become thoroughly conversant with the program and time should be set aside to identify target children and to organise rooms where small groups can be trained.

Counsellors or guidance personnel who may already have used similar programs with small groups of students should be consulted because they can help to train staff in this program if a substantial school-wide approach is to be adopted. At a more minimal level, such programs in schools and clinics are often implemented by counsellors and guidance personnel.

The three programs are fully described in the following sections and Table 6 summarises the setting and the relevant personnel required for each program.

Table 6   Program Application and Personnel Involved within a School or Clinical Setting

Program	Setting	Personnel
Talk Sense to Yourself program for conduct disorders	Individual or small-group setting. At school within the context of a school-based support program or at a guidance unit	Counsellors, guidance personnel or teachers involved in an in-school support team
Monitoring and Cueing program for behaviour change with conduct disorders	Classroom setting	All classroom teachers including support adviser teachers where applicable
On-Task Training program to improve attention span and organisation	Individual, group or whole-classroom setting or guidance unit	All classroom teachers including support adviser teachers and counselling or guidance personnel

Philosophy of Operations: Program Skills and the School Environment

The programs which will be presented largely address the issue of individual deficits. It is important, however, that schools recognise the interactional, organisational and curriculum variables which contribute to both the problem and the solution. Figure 3 identifies the factors involved. The skills-based approaches will help teachers and students to improve the quality of their interaction and to optimise learning, but it is also essential to address the other relevant factors.

The programs focus primarily on skills development for teachers and students. If a school support team is built, this adds to the organisational or systems approaches which each school can utilise. It should be recognised that conduct problems and attention deficit disorders are complex matters and that a simple answer to such problems will not be found in the implementation of a single program. Schools must deal with a range of issues so that a comprehensive and balanced approach to student welfare can be developed.

SYSTEMS AND ORGANISATIONAL ASPECTS	SKILLS DEVELOPMENT	CURRICULUM
Welfare policy Discipline policy Pastoral-welfare committee Support adviser team Talk Sense to Yourself approaches, etc.	FOR TEACHERS Interpersonal skills Classroom management Conflict resolution SPECIAL SKILLS e.g. Talk Sense to Yourself approaches, etc.	Allocation of time Materials Subjects offered Content, etc.

AN INTEGRATED AND BALANCED APPROACH TO STUDENT WELFARE

Figure 3 **Talk Sense to Yourself Program within an Overall Framework for the Development of Student Welfare in Schools**

3

Talk Sense to Yourself Program: Teaching Units

Starting the Program: Preliminary Considerations

The targets for this program are those children or adolescents whose disruptive behaviour at school is causing serious concern. The program has been used in primary schools from Year 5 upwards and across the whole range of the student population.

It is important that before a target child or adolescent is engaged in the program the following points are carefully considered:

- suitability for the program: voluntary or non-voluntary,
- criteria for skills development: mastery approaches,
- selection of the appropriate approach: individual or group work.

Suitability for the Program: Voluntary or Non-Voluntary

A number of options exist within a school environment regarding the involvement of students in this program. In high-school settings students who cause disruption usually find their way to a member of the school executive, a form or house patron and possibly the school counsellor or school principal. At any one of these levels students can be disciplined or 'spoken to' about their behaviour. Many such students are seen not by one but by several teachers or members of staff and it is a 'fair bet' that they are seen more than once in any given period.

By applying the Talk Sense to Yourself approach, the inefficient and ineffective method of dealing with these students by a series of ad hoc meetings can be changed to a carefully structured program offering many advantages. It is important to recognise, however, that no program can achieve results unless the participant co-operates. Work with the program should not proceed unless a spirit of collaboration exists and there is a level of voluntary commitment to beginning the program. This does not mean that the program can never be started unless the student knocks on a counsellor's door and asks for help. It is unusual for students to consult teachers or counsellors about conduct disorders because they are seldom aware of the nature of their problem.

Discussion should take place with the students regarding the problems created by their behaviour. The program should be outlined, and suggested to them as a means to help them to stay out of trouble and to achieve better school results. The approach may vary with the age and personality of the students involved. Some younger children or adolescents can be readily directed to the special program without arousing opposition. It is possible to be quite directive and to inform the student that he or she will be required to be involved in a short program. Older students may have to be persuaded of the value of the program and in many cases a considerable amount of 'disputing' will need to take place before voluntary participation is obtained.

The process of 'disputing' with a student is dealt with in the first stages of the program. The concept of 'disputing' is drawn from the work of Ellis (1962) in his rational-emotive therapy approach to challenging the maladaptive beliefs and attributions held by individuals. It is important to deal with the issue of behaviour and beliefs and 'dispute' with the adolescent about the effects his or her behaviour has on levels of functioning and attainments. The vast majority of children and adolescents 'agree' to try the program and in that sense they become voluntary participants.

However, a small number of children will refuse to participate. These children may either appear to be voluntary at the beginning but clearly indicate their unwillingness within one or two sessions, or they may refuse to participate at the outset. Unless the child or adolescent is prepared to co-operate, the program should not be started or continued. Further disputing or manipulating of school-based consequences may be necessary in order to change the student towards voluntary participation. Until he or she recognises the need to change, neither this nor any other program can be of help.

A framework for the whole program is shown in Figure 4. The program skills are clearly identified and the stages of voluntary or non-voluntary status are outlined. In many situations the timing of the initial approach may be wrong and an approach at a later date, or following the manipulation of consequences or sanctions, may produce the necessary movement towards voluntary status.

Criteria for Skills Development: Mastery Approaches

Talk Sense to Yourself is a mastery-based learning program. It identifies a number of cognitive and behavioural skills which participants are expected to learn and an evaluation of the level of skills acquisition is important. The concept of mastery training is significant. Children and adolescents learn at different rates and there is no one allocation of time which will be satisfactory for all learners. It is fairly obvious that learning the skills of reading is a task which requires time and patience. Results do not come overnight and the time needed by the quickest child to learn to read will differ considerably from that required by the slowest child. A teaching program must permit mastery of fundamental skills before moving on to the next level, and the same principle applies in an area of affective learning.

The skills in the program are there to be learnt and some adolescents or children may take two or three sessions to begin talking sense to themselves whilst others require twelve or thirteen sessions. The program should never be approached as a ten- or twelve-lesson unit where

NON-VOLUNTARY PATH	COGNITIVE SKILLS	BEHAVIOURAL TARGET SKILLS
• First dispute with student via the use of the key question . . . if no success . . .	• Learning key question: 'Is what I'm doing helping me?'	• Assertive not aggressive (a) understanding the assertiveness line (b) private and public approaches
• Ensure that consequences occur, e.g. sanctions exclusions parent interviews suspensions If still no success . . .	• Establishing goals to stop doing and to start doing

• The emotional-temperature graph: Weekly analysis | • Situational rehearsal Reacting to provocative statements In combination with Unit 9 and Student Exercise 5 |
| • The timing is wrong. Do not work with this person at this stage | • 'What am I thinking?' 'Is what I am thinking helping me?' 'Is it angry, is it sensible?' | • Resisting peer group pressure

• Organisational checklists |
	• Changing negative thinking (i) consequences (ii) calm thoughts (iii) control and confidence	• Other role plays or rehearsals as required
	• Cue sheets in books and memorised Posters for imaginary visualisation	
	• Learning more about how our beliefs affect our behaviour	
	• The expert adviser . . . learning to Talk Sense to Yourself	
	• Examining beliefs	
	• Further identification of student beliefs	
	• Script cards	
	• For younger children . . . 'Mr Trouble' and auto-suggestion	

Figure 4 **Overall Program for All Individuals**
The program starts for all individuals with the 'key question' and an offer of help via the Talk Sense to Yourself program. If this offer is accepted, the individual is voluntary . . . if not, he or she is seen as non-voluntary and may not start the program.

a new skill is taught each day. Rather, the skills should be taught to mastery before moving on to other elements in the program.

A final point as to what precisely constitutes mastery level: A level cannot be quantified in terms of a set figure. For some tasks which require memorisation of plans, calming self-statements, etc. a target of 75 to 80 per cent can be set but in other more general situations the determination of what constitutes mastery must be left to the teacher.

Group Work or One-to-One Approaches

The specific characteristics of adolescents make it particularly challenging to work with a group of them. They tend to be fairly active and
talkative, are affected by frequent mood swings, identity confusion or
diffuseness, increased sexual awareness and a varying need to gain
approval from their peers. These factors alone may create some difficulties but when the specific characteristics of behaviour and conduct disorder are added, the task of running such a group will be quite daunting
and in some cases almost impossible. Impulsiveness, aggression, disor-
ganisation, hyperactivity, immaturity, high reactivity and manipulative
behaviour call for special abilities in the group leader to focus the group
on the tasks of learning new skills and changing behaviour.

Group work may be inappropriate for some of the following situations
or reasons:

- The target children or adolescents cannot sufficiently control their
  behaviour in a group, so are merely trying to get attention from others
  all the time.

- The members of the group cannot delay their need to work out crisis
  issues which constantly occur.

- The group establishes a 'negative or anti' framework where members
  are only interested in demonstrating to the other members how 'bad'
  or 'out of control' they are.

- The group is too large. With a skills group the object is to learn to use
  skills and to suspend other issues and problems for one hour. The
  number in any group may be two or three and it is doubtful whether
  a larger group would be successful as control would become too big
  an issue, thus reducing skill-based learning.

Groups which run under the conditions mentioned above will do little
more than reinforce the already out-of-control behaviour being exhibited.
So much time is spent in trying to settle the group members and remind-
ing or redirecting them to the task that actual time on tasks is minimal.
With some adolescents, or mix of individuals, group work should not be
considered until they have had sufficient time in a one-to-one relationship to develop some control skills.

The problems and pitfalls of group work should not be regarded as
insurmountable and thus prevent teachers from running groups; it is

important, however, that these issues be recognised at the outset. An individual approach, although considerably less economical in terms of time and numbers of students, has proved to be successful in the early stages of the program. Later stages, involving behaviour rehearsal, are suited to group work but because of their more cognitive nature, the early teaching units are probably best begun at an individual level.

Checklist of Program Skills

The skills listed below should be taught to each student who is involved in the program. The skills are presented in a set sequence, starting with the cognitive unit and then moving into the behavioural skills. It is important that these skills be learnt to a level of mastery if the program is to be successful. Once the skill has been taught, subsequent checks on learning should take place and a mastery level of approximately 80 to 90 per cent should be set. If the target child fails to learn the specific task, the relevant unit should be taught again.

If after two or three revisions of the skill the target child is not at a satisfactory level, no further progress is likely to occur and motivation or voluntary status may need to be more closely examined.

COGNITIVE SKILLS **LEVEL OF LEARNING CHECK (%)**

1 Learning key question:
'Is what I'm doing helping me?'

2 Establishing goals:
To stop doing and to start doing.

3 Emotional-temperature chart and discomfort scale:
Weekly analysis.

4 Behaviour and beliefs:
Changing negative thinking.

5 Cue cards and posters.

6 More about how beliefs affect behaviour.

7 The expert adviser: learning to Talk Sense to Yourself.

8 Examining beliefs.

9 Further identification of student beliefs.

10 Script cards.

11 Additional approaches: 'Mr Trouble' and auto-suggestion.

(continued over page)

LEVEL OF LEARNING CHECK (%)

BEHAVIOUR REHEARSAL

1 Assertive not aggressive.

2 Situational rehearsal.

3 Resisting peer group pressure.

4 Organisational checklists.

Figure 5 **Individual Skills Checklist in Order of Presentation**

Cognitive Skills

UNIT 1 Learning the Key Question

Time required: 15 minutes
Format: 1:1 or small-group setting
Materials required: Key question display 'Is what I'm doing helping me?'

The program normally begins with a self-evaluation question which asks the students concerned to examine their behaviour in terms of its impact on themselves and on others. A key question asks the target students whether their behaviour is helpful. The primary object of this phase is the adolescents' awareness of their behaviour, and their inclination to change. At this stage the necessity of disputing may arise with students who are non-voluntary. It is important to describe the consequences of their misbehaviour and to challenge behaviours or beliefs which are clearly maladaptive.

FIRST KEY DISPLAY USED WITH TARGET CHILD

IS WHAT I'M DOING HELPING ME?

IS IT HELPFUL . . . IS IT REALLY O.K.?

The student should be given a copy of the key question 'Is what I'm doing helping me?' and asked to learn it.

This key question will be used again and again to ask the student to focus on his or her behaviour. It is used at the outset in 'disputing' to help to bring the adolescent to a clearer understanding of the need to evaluate what he or she is doing. It is used when in doubt. It is used continually and therefore needs to be memorised by the student.

Voluntary or Non-Voluntary?

The target child has now had the opportunity to recognise the problems his or her behaviour is causing and should be asked: 'Here is a program which can help you to stop the behaviours that are causing problems for you and for others. DO YOU WANT TO LEARN HOW TO CHANGE WITH MY HELP BY USING THIS PROGRAM?'

This question focuses the student back to the positive and offers help. Teachers using the program can of course use their own words to make the offer of help and the choice of phrasing is left to the user. The intention at this point and throughout the program is to permit flexibility so that the basic message or meaning is kept while allowing the surface structure to reflect each individual's style.

Following the offer of help by means of the program the vast majority of students choose to become voluntary. At this stage the first session is concluded. The student passes on to the next lesson unit when the second appointment time is scheduled (see the checklist of program skills) and at this second meeting, a little time should be allowed to check on progress.

If a student refuses the offer of help, he or she is regarded as non-voluntary and further disputing should take place at another time. If after one or even two more brief attempts to dispute and to obtain consent to work through the program the student still remains non-voluntary no further times are set. The student is given the opportunity of contacting the teacher at a later time and the 'door is left open' should a change of mind occur. In the meantime the school should continue to let the child experience the consequences of misbehaviour and a variety of other approaches can be tried (see Figure 4). If these are finally unsuccessful, it means that the teacher and the program are unable to help.

UNIT 2 Establishing Goals

Time required: 15–20 minutes
Format: 1:1 or small-group setting
Materials required: Example of Goal Sheet
After the target student has concentrated on the key question 'Is what I'm doing helping me?' and has had the opportunity to realise that a change of behaviour is needed, it is important to focus on the behaviours to be stopped. This can be done by making up a goal sheet listing behaviours to stop and to start.

Student Exercise 1: Goal Sheets

You need to have clear goals to work towards. Sometimes goals can be expressed in two ways: Don't do — or Do — X, e.g.:

GOALS	GOALS
STOP DOING	*START DOING*
1 Calling out in lessons.	— Put my hand up. — Keep my mouth closed.
2 Getting into hassles with other kids because I'm always near them.	— Stay in my seat. — Sit away from most kids. — Avoid Peter/Paul . . .
3 Thinking negative/fed up thoughts.	— Think positively. — Change my attitudes.
4 Arguing with the teacher.	— Accept the teacher's decisions.

Now can you figure out the kinds of goals which apply to you? Rough out some ideas below, then make up your own goal sheets to put into bags, books, etc . . . and to learn!

GOALS

STOP DOING   *START DOING*

....

....

....

....

....

UNIT 3 Emotional-Temperature Chart and Discomfort Scale

Time required: 20 minutes
Format: 1:1 or small-group setting
Materials required: A copy of the Emotional-Temperature Chart and Discomfort Scale and Student Exercise 2.
The object of this scale is to let the target student become aware of his or her level of arousal. The emotional-temperature chart has a one-to-ten scale which permits individuals to identify their levels of anger or discomfort in a given situation or setting. Each student should learn to identify how he or she feels in a variety of classrooms and the first task is to explain the scale and to ask the student to rate each situation.

As the scale increases, a 'loss of control line' can be seen. If students reach this line they usually become extremely angry and irrational. At this point it is not possible to talk sense to them because they are far too emotional. The intention of the Talk Sense to Yourself program is to prevent target students from losing control of their behaviour. It is hoped that this can be accomplished by building in some skills of self-instruction and reflection regarding the appropriate way to act.

Bringing the levels of arousal or discomfort to awareness can be valuable in itself because the target student can begin to note which circumstances produce high levels of anger or discomfort. Awareness often helps the student to be more vigilant regarding the need to practise some of the self-control skills which are going to be taught as the program proceeds.

Two or three applications of the program can be used in conjunction with the teaching step of bringing the emotional-temperature chart to awareness.

Emotional-Temperature Chart and Discomfort Scale

10 Boiling point

9 ············ loss of control line ············

8 Very angry or uncomfortable

7 Angry

6
 Steaming up or not too happy
5

4 so-so

3 O.K.

2 Calm and fine and feeling good

1

Student Exercise 2: Activities

1 The student should understand the emotional-temperature chart and discomfort scale sufficiently so that he or she can give a simple explanation of its purpose.
2 Ask the student to keep a daily diary of levels in a number of classes. The act of monitoring can be a powerful tool which can produce positive changes in arousal levels.
3 Ask the student to fill in a blank timetable with levels for each class during the week. This will at least identify the at-risk areas and pinpoint the times when cue cards and scripts, etc. (later units of the program) should be used.
4 Follow the timetable analysis with the suggestion that in any two at-risk periods the student should try to concentrate on a plan (such as reviewing the goal sheets). Students should try to improve their temperature levels. Sometimes it is possible to suggest an upper limit above which not to let themselves go. This can be a valuable self-fulfilling prophecy.

UNIT 4 Behaviour and Beliefs: Changing Negative Thinking

Time required: 40 minutes
Format: 1:1 or group setting
Materials required: Two cartoons 'What Do You Think?' and 'Talk Sense to Yourself' plus three white cards on which to write out the consequence, calm thoughts and control statements.

In order to help the individual to change his or her behaviour it is important to recognise that there is usually an underlying belief which determines the behaviour in question. An example of a belief that underlies maladaptive behaviour might be:

'It is not fair — I don't have to be treated like that. Who does he think he is? He's just a rotten pig!' etc.

It is important to discover what the target individual is thinking as in nine out of ten cases these beliefs are maladaptive and will need to be challenged and changed.

Methods of Discovering Beliefs (1)

Materials required: First cartoon: 'What do you think?'

The small cartoon can be used to elicit thinking. Ask the students to describe their thoughts or feelings in relation to the kind of incident which is outlined in the cartoon. You will probably have to lead them as they are often embarrassed to say things like:

> I'm fed up of this rubbish . . . can't stand X . . .
> He's a rotten teacher, always picking on me . . .
> What a turkey, I'm not going to do what he wants . . .
> Why should I . . . It's a joke . . .
> I wish he'd drop dead . . .
> He's not going to push me around . . .
> Ignore him, this is a waste of time . . . I've had it . . .

Make statements such as the above and ask whether these are the kinds of thoughts that are occurring.

Now fill in three bubbles with a selection of maladaptive thoughts.

Ask the child or adolescent these questions:

- Are those thoughts helping you?
- Are they angry thoughts?
- Can you predict the consequences for someone who holds these thoughts?

At this point move quickly on to the next part of the exercise.

Cue Cards (2)

Materials required: Cartoon sheets, and six to eight small white index cards for writing on.

The objective of the cue cards will become obvious. Use Card 1 to write down the consequences. Again you need to help and lead the child so that a clear chain of consequences can be written. Do not show the finished cue cards to the student at this stage but build up the consequences with the aid of the student on one of the white index cards.

On the second card get the child to write up to five or six calming statements. Ask the student to indicate what he or she might say to calm down a friend. Again you can help, but it is far better to try to ensure that the personal constructs you use are applicable to the target child. If you say 'relax', for example, this means something to you but to a thirteen-year-old with no concept of 'relaxation' it may not be very useful. He may use an expression such as 'hang loose'.

On the third card try to elicit words tied into control and confidence. Describe a football game or a netball match and ask the student to imagine that the opposition is tough. What words of encouragement and help would the coach give?

> 'Oh heck . . . these guys are too good, we'll never beat them. It's a waste of time.'

Words like that would hardly be expected to boost morale. It is important that a feeling of confidence or impression of being in control is given:

> 'We can handle it . . . sure they're good but if we stay calm it'll be O.K. We can do it . . . No risk . . . No worries.'

Use examples such as these or others that spring to mind and write them down on the card as examples of control and confidence statements.

Now put all three cards out under the first cartoon 'What do you think?' and produce the second cartoon entitled; 'Talk Sense to Yourself'.

- Write into the first empty bubble — Consequences
- Write into the second empty bubble — Calm thoughts
- Write into the third empty bubble — Control/confidence thoughts

Now once more ask the child the questions:

- Are those thoughts helping you?
- Are they angry thoughts?
- Can you predict the consequences for someone who holds these thoughts?

CONSEQUENCES

If I lose control/get
into trouble
- I'll be out of class
- I could be sent to
the deputy/princrpal
- Back where I started
- Letter sent home and
Mum/dad feel bad
- I feel low, angry, etc.
- I could be suspended
or expelled
- No reference, no job
no $, holidays, cars.

**✿ CUE CARDS MUST
BE LEARNT**

CALM THOUGHTS

- Take it easy
- Calm down
- Relax
- It's not worth it
- Hang in there
- Cool it
- Count to 10
- Take 4 deep breaths

**CONTROL AND
CONFIDENCE**

- I can do it
- I can handle it
(pressure)
- I'm O.K. - I'm under
control
- No risk, No worries
- No problems
Etc.

**✿ USE THEM IN
BOOKS**

✿ REHEARSE THEM AT HOME

At this point you have tried to make the target student aware of his or her thinking and related it to behaviour. This concept will need to be reworked many times so that the child or adolescent is aware of the self-guiding function of inner speech. Several other units pick up the idea that behaviour is directly influenced by thoughts.

When conducting this exercise it is not unusual for a child to indicate that it is not aware of its thoughts. This does not matter because the three blocks of consequences, calm, and control self-statements can then be introduced as important beliefs to hold.

Now the child or adolescent is asked to copy down the three sets of ideas on to the small cards. These will be referred to as cue cards and the child has the task of learning the contents of the cards.

The target child is expected to learn for the next session as many of the self-guiding statements as possible — UP TO 80 PER CENT MASTERY. These cards are of no use unless the ideas are internalised — learnt. The learning process will often take two or three sessions and the teacher will provide added opportunities to memorise the ideas as the next units are taught.

It is not necessary that all the self-guiding statements are learnt and the teacher should help the target student to decide which appear most relevant. It is sufficient to select four or five of the calm statements and the control statements, but expect a 90 per cent memorisation of the consequence chain.

UNIT 5 Cue Cards and Posters

Time required: 30–40 minutes
Format: 1:1 or group setting
Materials required: Cue cards used in the previous unit plus the copy of the poster on page 59. (It may also be worthwhile to acquire several pictures of beautiful scenes, horses, skiers, football stars, etc.)
This unit is really a continuation of the previous lesson which worked with self-guiding statements. The child or adolescent has had a few days to learn (or forget) the self-statements written on to the three cue cards. The first job is to test the level of memorisation reached. Remove the cards and ask the student to go through the chains, and record these results on the child's skills checklist. It is often a good idea to go over the statements two or three times by reading them to the student and then to go through the test again in order to help the process of internalisation.

The cue cards should be written in black because the cards can be used in the student's exercise books where they are placed under the page currently being used. The thick black writing normally permits the words to be visible to the student without other boys or girls being able to notice them. The cards can now be used as cueing devices by which the student obtains a constant reminder of the sensible things to think.

Cueing can go a lot further. The guiding statements all begin with the letter 'C'. This letter can be used in a number of ways to help the target

student to stay out of trouble. If the chains have been sufficiently learnt, the three titles bring into awareness the ideas contained on the cue cards.

Consequences

Calm thoughts

Control or confidence thoughts

The 'C' can be written by the student on a small card and displayed on the desk. It can be written on a piece of paper which is then wound around a pen or pencil that will be used. The variations are numerous and can be tailored to the situation and to the individual.

Use of the Posters

To this stage the concept of 'talking sense to yourself' has been introduced through the cue cards but it is now important to develop the concept further. The displays which directly refer to talking sense and giving yourself good advice should be used and related to some of the self-guiding statements learnt in the cue cards. The concept of 'talking sense' has been relatively specific but as the program develops further, more varied and conceptually organised approaches will be used.

The two statements, 'Talk Sense to Yourself' and 'Give Yourself Good Advice', should again be committed to memory and the target students by now can be expected to have copies of the following, which have been learnt:

Is what I'm doing helping me?
Think consequences.
Think calm thoughts.
Think control and confidence.
Talk sense to yourself.
Give yourself good advice.

Two relatively large posters should be made. They can be made in a variety of ways and the size may range from a minimum of A4 up to that of a commercially available poster.

The posters require a central theme which is acceptable to the student and at the same time displays a calm or inspirational picture(s). Useful pictures can sometimes be found on old calendars or in magazines and they can be mounted on the poster card. In the past, students have selected a wide variety of pictures including snow-capped mountains, beaches, surf waves, trees, wild horses, skiers, motorcycle stunts, etc. Pictures showing violence or aggressive acts, e.g. Rambo or a Kung Fu fighter, are definitely out! The picture should be regarded by the student as calming or 'cool' and possibly as inspirational in some way. Some students have selected a montage of pictures which have tended to tell a story with a salutary or sobering message; once again the variations are endless.

The poster is then further developed by writing four or five of the 'Talk Sense to Yourself' statements on or around the central picture with coloured textas. It is important to include the first key question as well as the 'Talk Sense to Yourself' statements. In addition several of the cue card statements should be selected by the student and added to the poster. The poster is placed on a wall and the student practises recalling the details with eyes closed.

The poster visualisation process should be continued until mastery levels are achieved and the student is able to re-create the poster and its written messages in various locations even in the absence of the poster. A number of imagined 'poster hangings' should be enacted on blackboards, walls, and even on the shirt or dress of the teacher in front of the class. The size of the poster should also be a focus of attention, as should its brightness. The student should be encouraged to imagine the

poster expanding to fill almost a whole wall and particular words should glow or become like neon signs.

The object of these procedures is twofold: to learn the Talk Sense to Yourself self-guiding statements and to teach the child or adolescent to self-visualise as an added aid to controlling behaviour. The student is taught to 'hang' the poster in imagination in specific situations which have been identified with the emotional-temperature chart as threatening. The student may consider certain subjects and teachers as creating problems so it is important to get the student to visualise the particular classroom and to practise hanging the poster in imagination. In some circumstances it may even be advisable physically to go to the room and really hang the poster in order to create a concrete reference point. The target student and the teacher adviser can go to the room and 'hang' the poster when school is finished and the other students and teachers have gone home.

Posters and a variety of cueing devices on pens, cards or books should provide a substantial set of control cues to help the student to start concentrating on self-discipline.

UNIT 6 More About How Beliefs Affect Behaviour

Time required: 15–20 minutes
Format: 1:1 or group setting
Materials required: Beliefs Cause Behaviour exercise
This unit is designed further to help a student to recognise the powerful influence thinking has over behaviour.

Each of the examples uses the *A B C* approach mentioned by Ellis (1962), where *A* is an event, *B* is a belief or attitude, and *C* is the reaction which results from the belief. In the exercise, however, two actions are given to each situation and the target child is expected to supply the beliefs probably being thought for each action. In addition the child or adolescent is expected to make a comment on the beliefs as 'sensible and helpful' or as 'not helpful and not sensible'.

Student Exercise 3: Beliefs Cause Behaviour

See whether you can supply the beliefs which make Tony act the way he does. Note that there are two possible behaviours and it is necessary to supply two different sets of beliefs.

Event	Tony sees two boys coming towards him
Behaviour	1 he clears off fast
	2 he continues on his way
Belief	1
	2

Event	Tanya is bumped by another girl in the yard
Behaviour	1 she pushes the girl and hits her
	2 she tells her to 'watch out'
Belief	1
	2

Event	Tony goes to the oval to try out for the football team but when he gets there he sees about 30 other guys
Behaviour	1 he walks away without even trying out 2 he gets changed to play
Belief	1 2

Event	Tanya is approached by two girls who suggest that they 'wag' the rest of the afternoon
Behaviour	1 she 'wags' the rest of the afternoon 2 she remains at school and goes to class
Belief	1 2

Event	Tom is in a class with a young relief teacher and the other kids are giving her a hard time
Behaviour	1 Tom says to the teacher, 'Hey, Miss, have you heard the joke about the dog with only three legs?' 2 Tom says to the class 'Give it a rest, let the teacher have a fair go.'
Belief	1 2

UNIT 7 The Expert Adviser

Time required: 15–20 minutes
Format: 1:1 setting only
Materials required: Ensure that three chairs are in position.
In trying to get the children to give themselves good advice and to talk sense to themselves, the use of 'The Expert' can be valuable.

Arrange the chairs so that you sit directly behind the target child's head at an angle of 45 degrees to the child's chair. Explain that from this position you can give good advice and that you have decided to allocate a week or so actually to accompany the child to school and almost everywhere else in order to provide expert advice to keep the child out of trouble.

This will usually produce an amazed, embarrassed and unbelieving

POSITIONING OF THE THREE CHAIRS FOR THE 'EXPERT'

TALKING SENSE TO THE STUDENT

SEATED BEHIND GIVE HER GOOD ADVICE!

stare. Clearly, for you to do this would be quite impossible but at this stage the target child may be unsure whether you are really serious. Ninety-nine per cent of children would be immensely embarrassed if you were to carry out your stated intentions; it is important, however, that you build up this belief for five to ten minutes. Give examples of provoking situations and offer advice from your seated position. Then check your diary and tell the child that you cannot in fact act as his or her expert because you have some other engagements, but say also that you will find someone who is able to spend at least a few days as his or her personal adviser. You need to tell the child that the person who will act as personal adviser knows the child exceptionally well. Ask the child to suggest someone who is an expert on, and knows and really understands him or her.

At the next session, tell the child that you have contacted someone who is willing to act as the child's adviser and accompany him or her for a week or so. Ask the child again to suggest who this person might be. Then look at your watch and tell the child that this person will be there in two minutes. Get out a chair for this person.

Ask the child to step outside the room with you and meet his or her 'expert'. In the corridor express surprise that the expert has not arrived and go back into the room, but be sure to get the child into the expert's chair. Say 'You sit there, please' and direct the child to the vacant chair. Then sit down and address the child in this manner: 'Well, thank you for coming. You have agreed to act as adviser to (name and subject). I wonder if you could give him or her some important advice, etc.'

Keep the charade going for as long as possible and until the fact has sunk in that (a) the child is its own expert adviser, and (b) the child must give good advice to itself.

Go through several provocative situations and get the child to give 'good advice' to itself from the expert's chair. If necessary, you take over the expert's chair and show the child how to give good advice to itself.

UNIT 8 Examining Beliefs

Time required: 15 minutes
Format: 1:1 or group setting (this unit can also be given as a homework assignment)
Materials required: Examining Beliefs and Behaviour exercise.
A range of inappropriate and maladaptive beliefs maintain and support dysfunctional behaviour. It is important to challenge and retrain these beliefs. The practice exercise explained below is useful in helping students to identify beliefs which may be the cause of dysfunctional behaviour.

Student Exercise 4: Examining Beliefs and Behaviour

Decide whether the beliefs listed below are helpful or not by predicting what kind of behaviour and resulting consequences will flow from them. Where a behaviour is listed, supply the likely beliefs and consequences.

BELIEF	BEHAVIOUR	CONSEQUENCES
I hate maths it's boring		
	will not wait in line, pushes in, demands things immediately, impatient and will not wait	
if a kid calls me a name that's bad for them, they're dead		
	does not turn up for detentions or any other punishments	
when it's boring I like to muck up just for some fun		
	argues with teachers about being told off for talking or not working	
okay so I got into trouble I'll just have to cop the consequences		
	gets into arguments with other kids, often fights	

BELIEF

if I can't get my own
way I won't play with
other kids

BEHAVIOUR

will not do as told and
has no respect for
teachers

CONSEQUENCES

teachers are unfair
they pick on me and
don't give me a fair
go

never cleans up the
bedroom at home,
leaves a big mess
everywhere

I don't like some
subjects but I know I
need to finish school
to get my certificate

when things go
wrong it's not real
good but I can cope

UNIT 9 Further Identification of Student Beliefs

Time required: 20–30 minutes
Format: 1:1 setting only
Materials required: Finish These Sentences exercise.

The object of this short exercise is to try to identify whether the beliefs held by target students are likely to cause problems. The exercise can be completed verbally or in a written form. The student is given a series of unfinished sentences and his or her job is to supply as quickly as possible the first response that comes to mind. It is often a good idea to go through the unfinished sentences a second time in an attempt to obtain more information.

Once the sentences have been completed, the same procedure as outlined in the previous exercises should be followed and the beliefs should be examined in relation to their value or helpfulness.

If some or all of the sentences are completed it is important to evaluate each belief with the student in question and if necessary dispute the sense or worth of obviously dysfunctional beliefs. Alternative beliefs need to be substituted where appropriate.

Student Exercise 5: Finish These Sentences

1 I think that school is . . . . . .
2 Something I can't stand at school is . . . . . .
3 Teachers are . . . . . .
4 One thing I really hate is when teachers . . . . . .
5 If I don't like a teacher I'll . . . . . .
6 If a teacher picks on me I'll . . . . . .
7 I won't work when . . . . . .
8 If I get put on detention or punishment I . . . . . .
9 I feel like wagging when . . . . . .
10 I only refuse to do as I'm told when . . . . . .
11 Something that makes me angry is . . . . . .
12 When I get angry I'll . . . . . .
13 I get into trouble when I'm with . . . . . .
14 I muck up because . . . . . .

UNIT 10 Script Cards

Time required: 30–40 minutes
Format: 1:1 or small-group setting
Materials required: Two small white cards and a copy of the two scripts as examples.

These cards are extensions of the cue cards. They provide a specific direction regarding behaviour and the way to think and cope. We are aware that a script is usually obtained by actors and actresses who play a part in a play. There are cues to be memorised, and this script is the same. The child must memorise the text.

When writing a script keep it simple and brief. One paragraph only. Include the following:

- A description of the way this person behaves in general (a description in a nutshell).
- A statement of what the person says to him or herself — Talk Sense to Yourself.
- Statements of precisely how the person copes with certain provocative situations or problems, i.e. what he or she actually says or does in these situations.

A script can be constructed to reflect the needs of children or adolescents with particular problems. Thus a child who is angry or aggressive may get Calm Colin or Friendly Farrah.

Calm Colin
Colin never gets angry. He is calm, and easy to get along with. When other kids try to upset him he smiles and says to himself: 'Calm down — don't get uptight — it's not worth it'. If Colin is called a name he says: 'Yeah — mate, whatever you say' or he just ignores it. In lines outside class he doesn't worry about bumping or jostling, etc.

Friendly Farrah
Farrah likes meeting other kids and making friends. She can cope with unfriendly remarks by thinking to herself that not everyone is interested in being friendly and so she doesn't let it worry her. Farrah goes up to kids she hasn't met and smiles at them and introduces herself. She asks about their interests, hobbies, etc. She will offer to lend her textas, and quite often she may help others to do things. If she is hurt or insulted by others she takes a casual and friendly approach by not calling names and by saying, 'O.K. maybe some other time', etc.

Again, these scripts have to be learnt but there is no need for the child to be word-perfect; as long as the main themes are present the script is considered as mastered.

Using the Scripts

Once a script suitable for the specific target child has been designed (and these above scripts are only examples to be used as references), a decision is made regarding the appropriate time and place to use it. If the child or adolescent is experiencing a major problem in relation to fighting and arguing with certain peers, a set time is agreed upon when the acting is to take place. At this stage the student is asked to take on the role for a short time. Some students find it difficult to play a new role for more than three or four minutes while others may believe they can handle the role for a period or even a whole morning. Start from their comfort level and go for a length of time they feel happy about. Agree upon a set starting time so that the subject understands his or her job and its duration clearly.

In some situations, it is possible to use a set cue to start the role. It could be when you, as a visiting teacher, go into the classroom to ask the subject's teacher for something; it could be in the playground when lining up for lunch, or at any prearranged signal. Schedule a time to see how the new role trial went as soon as possible after it has taken place. If practicable, try to extend the time at the next role-play period so that the new role will begin to feel a little more natural. If the role did not work out try to decide what skill is lacking or what circumstances need to be changed. Continue with additional trials until the new role is working. When this stage is reached it is fairly easy to ask the student to continue using the role in circumstances where it is clearly of value.

UNIT 11 Additional Approaches

Time required: 30 minutes plus additional sessions
Format: 1:1 or group setting
Materials required: None.

Mr Trouble (For Younger Children)

A valuable approach with younger children is to 'personalise' the angry thoughts or irrational and unhelpful beliefs. The thoughts can be referred to as 'tricky thoughts' or as Mr Angry, Mr Nonsense, or any phrase that conjures up a sneaky person out to cause trouble. The irrational beliefs or ideas which will cause the child to get into trouble are invested with a sense of malevolence and delight as they try to trick the child into mischief.

The child is instructed to watch out for Mr Trouble, who will attempt to get control of its thinking and trap it into thinking 'silly' thoughts. He will try to usurp control from Mr Sensible and replace it with nonsense and argumentativeness.

It is important for the child to understand that the way Mr Nonsense gets control is by suggesting to the child a variety of ideas which are not very helpful. The child will catch himself or herself thinking, for example:

> 'I can't stand it when . . .'
> 'I hate my teacher'
> 'Nobody understands me'
> 'All the rest of the kids treat me unfairly'
> 'If I don't get my own way it will be terrible', etc.

The child should be given a number of maladaptive statements which could indicate a Mr Angry trick to produce trouble. The statements can then be hidden amongst several coping and sensible statements, and the target child is asked to identify them.

> 'O.K., if I don't get what I want I'll cope'
> 'No-one in the school cares a damn about me'
> 'Why should we have to do "X" . . . I can't stand it'
> 'I really dislike it when I'm in trouble'
> 'I really hate Mr . . . he always picks on me'
> 'I don't like Mr . . . but I am not going to let that worry me', etc.

The concept of the 'trickster' or cunning Mr Nonsense who tries to take

control in certain situations can be readily developed with younger children to the point where they accept the image into their own vocabulary. It is of paramount importance that each child recognises the 'tricky nature' of the prankster and learns to be on guard against the really sneaky ways in which he or she will attempt to take control. The concept of keeping control must be equally developed by using the key statements:

- Is what I am thinking (doing) going to help?
- Talk sense to myself
- Give myself good advice

The child can be helped to keep control by being taught that Mr Trouble, Mr Nonsense etc. can quickly be sent packing by a very simple manoeuvre; all the child needs to do is repeat any two of the above sensible statements. These statements once repeated (in the child's head) send the nonsense ideas running for cover because the statements are very powerful. You can practise by suggesting to the child that he or she behaves incorrectly and thinks angry or unhelpful thoughts; the child should then repeat the two statements aloud quickly to dispel the 'nonsense' it hears.

Auto-Suggestion

Auto-suggestion techniques are usually linked to relaxation training and for some children who find it difficult to stay calm, the use of a tape recorder to train them to relax may be of value. Calming statements are read and recorded on to tape. Sometimes a guided fantasy occurs in which the target student selects certain scenes such as walking on a beach or relaxing in a pleasant rural setting. The voice on the tape can be the student's, the support-adviser teacher's or even that of one of the child's parents.

The object is to place on tape many calming and controlling self-instructional statements so that the child becomes familiar with the kinds of statements which need to be made. This tape can actually be used when the classroom teacher notices that the individual is becoming angry or unsettled. The child can be asked to leave the room and go to an office or nearby quiet area to listen to the tape.

The tape can also be used as a learning device. The target child is asked to play the recording at night just before going to bed. After two or three nights the statements should become familiar and therefore it is hoped that the child will be better able to incorporate the calming self-statements into a daily routine.

The recording should repeat many of the cue card statements previously learnt and these familiar statements should be linked to an issue or problem area. A scene is imagined and then the teacher or counsellor introduces a specific concern or problem and immediately suggests that the child will hear certain words.

'When you begin to feel even the slightest bit angry and feel like leaving the room you will hear these words:

> It's O.K. — you can handle it . . .
> take it easy and relax . . .
> breathe slowly and calm down . . .'

This approach to preparing a child for difficult situations can be used when required. The tape can relax the child and go through two or three guided fantasies which incorporate problems commonly experienced by the individual. The child should be encouraged to imagine hearing the tape or seeing its poster. The Talk Sense to Yourself statements taken from the cue cards should be applied to relevant situations and the child should then be given a small homework task of trying to imagine the voice or poster in situ.

Behaviour Rehearsal

UNIT 1 Assertive not Aggressive

Time required: 30 minutes +
Materials required: A copy of the Assertiveness Line.
In Unit 10 (Script Cards), one of the techniques used by the student is that of role-playing. To rehearse what he or she will say when the time comes is also valuable by teaching the student specific skills such as making friendly remarks or rebutting an insult.

Behaviour rehearsal often uses role-play approaches to try to teach appropriate ways of interaction. It is essential to the program and should be used regularly to provide training in social skills for students who have difficulty with student-teacher and student-student interactions.

When to Use Role-Play and Behaviour Rehearsal

The skills in this program tend to be laid out in a set order and in general the cognitive skills should be taught first while behaviour rehearsal and role-play are used towards the end of the program. In practice once the elements of the program are learnt cognitive self-instruction and behaviour rehearsal can become more closely integrated and the timing of role-plays can become flexible. Brief behaviour rehearsals can be useful fairly early in the program.

Conduct disordered adolescents tend to over-react and are often quite aggressive in their dealings with peers, and sometimes with teachers and other significant adults. In role-play and behaviour rehearsal it is helpful to have a scale or measure which can provide a framework to guide each student. The assertiveness line, a ten-point scale which identifies appropriate behaviour as well as aggressive and passive behaviour, serves this purpose. The use of a continuum as a constant reference point enables students to obtain feedback regarding their practice.

The assertiveness line is carefully explained to the students and they are asked to describe some of their past and current behaviour in terms of a one-to-ten score. At this stage it is important to spend some time discussing the messages which can be sent in a non-verbal way. Non-verbal signals such as frowns, grimaces, and body position can be described to make the point that people also send messages which can be given a one-to-ten score. Where possible, the teacher should demonstrate the kind of non-verbal behaviours which could get a student into trouble and after demonstrating a behaviour the student should be asked to give each expression a score and to try to put the non-verbal message into words.

THE ASSERTIVENESS SCALE

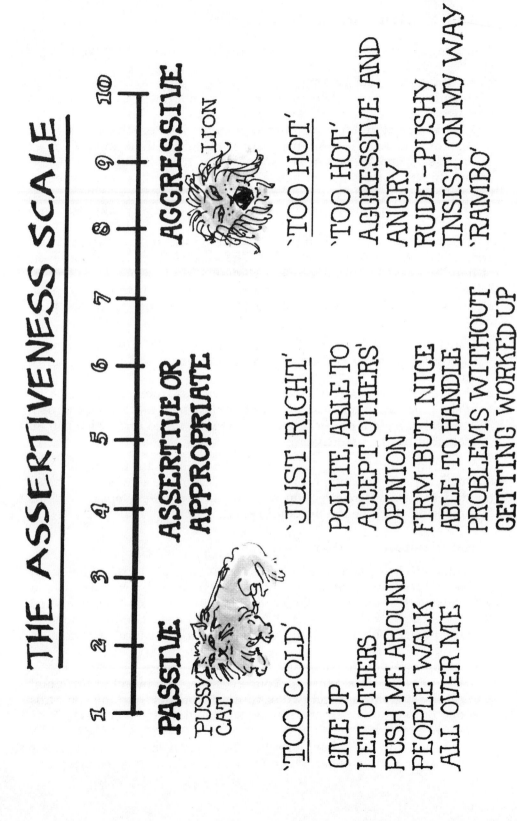

1 2 3 4 5 6 7 8 9 10

PASSIVE
PUSSY CAT

ASSERTIVE OR APPROPRIATE

AGGRESSIVE
LION

'TOO COLD'

GIVE UP
LET OTHERS
PUSH ME AROUND
PEOPLE WALK
ALL OVER ME

'JUST RIGHT'

POLITE, ABLE TO
ACCEPT OTHERS'
OPINION
FIRM BUT NICE
ABLE TO HANDLE
PROBLEMS WITHOUT
GETTING WORKED UP

'TOO HOT'

'TOO HOT'
AGGRESSIVE AND
ANGRY
RUDE – PUSHY
INSIST ON MY WAY
'RAMBO'

D

UNIT 2 Situational Rehearsal

Time required: 30–40 minutes initially plus additional time at later stages
Format: 1:1 or group setting
Materials required: 20 Provocative Statements (these can be given as homework after explanation and demonstration).

The behaviour of conduct disordered students is often characterised by an inability to consider the consequences of their actions and they react in aggressive and inappropriate ways. They react impulsively to perceived threats, insults and criticism with anger, hostility and invective. Once the level of emotional temperature shoots up there is no way of stopping the 'explosion' and these individuals very quickly get into trouble.

The object of this unit is further to develop the ability to 'talk sense' and to focus on behaviour rehearsal. The exercise tries to reduce levels of impulsiveness by building into a student's reaction phase the step of reflecting upon self-direction and control. A series of provocative situations is presented to students. Each of these situations is reacted to in two ways:

1 The student is asked to 'Talk Sense to Yourself' in order to create an appropriate level of self-control and to develop a self-guiding plan of action.
2 The student takes part in a behaviour rehearsal role-play in which he or she practises a response to the situation which has been described. A verbal or even a physical response may be called for, which is then evaluated on the assertiveness scale.

A second objective is to develop the ability to generalise self-instructional skills and appropriateness-evaluation to new situations. As the student becomes aware of the steps required and develops these skills by practising, such generalisation begins to occur.

Generalisation Training

The situations listed below represent a cross-section of those which occur in schools. Numerous situations which can be used by each teacher or school using this program will arise in relation to specific individuals and settings. They may already have arisen and been reacted to inappropriately, but they should be added to the situations provided in this book.

To begin, present the first situation to the student.

Next comes the Talk Sense to Yourself stage. The object at this point is to get the student to select two or three statements from the cue cards plus one or two other self-control and self-guiding statements which he or she can make up.

Now proceed to the behaviour rehearsal stage. If the situation calls for a verbal response or a particular facial expression or movement this should be role-played, and then feedback and direct instructions given as required to obtain an appropriate response.

The responses can also be given to students as a written exercise and then the teacher can ask the student to read each of the situations and the responses aloud before proceeding to the rehearsal stage. A number of variations can be used with the exercise, involving both written and memorised responses, but as one of the main objectives is to develop generalisation skills, written responses need not be memorised exactly. If the student can use a number of appropriate self-guiding statements, the objectives of the exercise are met. The ability to generalise can be tested further by asking for responses to newly devised situations once the target student has learnt the two-part approach of first using self-guiding speech and then appropriate-behaviour rehearsal.

Public and Private Approaches

When training an individual to inhibit aggressive behaviour, it is necessary to talk about the appropriate time and place. In almost every case it is inappropriate to take on a teacher in a classroom, no matter whether assertively or politely. This should only be done privately so that confrontation is avoided.

The student must learn how to negotiate with a teacher an appropriate time to speak about the matter.

> 'Please, sir, can I talk to you privately?'
> 'No, not now, James.'
> 'Well, could you suggest a time?'
> 'Oh, okay, come and see me at recess.'

Having established a time, it is important to practise stating the issue or concern. One way of doing this is to rehearse the use of an 'I' statement.

An 'I' Statement

When you (describe behaviour)
I feel (describe the feeling)
because (say why you feel like this)

Example:

> Being picked upon
> When you pick on me
> I feel angry and unhappy
> because it isn't fair

It is very important to focus on non-verbal behaviour, not only now but also at other times because a student's tone of voice, positive expressions, etc. can be regarded as aggressive and thus lead to retaliation by the teacher.

Practise discriminating postures, expressions, etc. and get the student to evaluate these in relation to the one-to-ten assertiveness scale.

The teacher should model inappropriate voice tone, aggressive stance, etc. and ask the target child to evaluate the 'message' sent by the body language with a mark between one and ten.

Written Format Used for Provocative Situations

SITUATION EXAMPLE	TALK SENSE TO YOURSELF (what I would say to myself)	BEHAVIOUR (what I would do)
name-calling	stay calm . . . it's not worth fighting about . . . take it easy . . . talk to him about it	say 'yeah mate'

Examples of Provocative Situations

1 A boy or girl calls you a name.

2 You are trying to finish your work while others in the class are fooling around. One of the other kids says 'look at . . . he's the teacher's pet . . . he's doing the work . . . crawler!'

3 You are in the playground and accidentally get knocked by another kid who is not watching where she is going. She runs into you . . . you feel angry but you say to yourself . . .

4 You are going to be late for a class and you know the teacher will get angry. You feel like wagging that lesson. What can you say to yourself? What will you do?

5 A girl accuses you of doing something you didn't do, e.g. moving her bag.

6 Another boy and girl have (you think) started an unpleasant rumour about you. You hear others calling you the names . . . and the boy is in your next class.

7 You have forgotten to bring some homework or an assignment to school and today the teacher is in an angry mood. You have done most of the assignment but it is at home and the teacher will probably not believe you did it.

8 You get to class and find that some kids have hidden your bag.

9 You have been wasting time and talking. The teacher tells you that she will send you out of class. You think that's unfair and a bit rough although the lesson is boring.

10 One of your teachers ignores others who are talking and picks on you most of the time (n.b. private approach).

11 One of your friends dobs you in for doing something. You say to your friend . . .

12 You are at home trying to work but your brother or sister is playing really loud music which stops you from concentrating.

13 You need more time to finish an assignment but the teacher may not believe that you couldn't get the books you needed.

14 Another kid pushes in front of you in a line at the canteen. You feel like throwing him out of the line and hitting him.

15 Other kids in the class are blaming you for causing the whole group to be in trouble when it was everyone's decision to talk and muck up.

16 The teacher tells you that you must stay in for detention but you have to be home as your cousins, whom you have not seen for years, are coming to your house at that time.

17 You have not understood the teacher's explanation regarding how to do a certain piece of work. You could ask the boy next to you but if you talk you could be in trouble; you could ask the teacher but she doesn't like going over the work again.

18 You are told to see the deputy principal who accuses you of doing something you didn't do but he tells you that two other kids said you threw someone else's bag into a creek.

19 You have been talking and have been sent out for misbehaviour. The teacher is going to put you on detention (which you think is a bit strong).

20 A relief teacher will be taking your class. Two friends suggest that you cut classes and go to their house because the relief teacher won't know that you're missing.

UNIT 3 Resisting Peer Group Pressure

Time required: 40 minutes initially plus additional time to develop mastery

Format: Group setting

Materials required: Large sheets of paper which can be held and used as cue sheets.

It is important to employ behaviour-rehearsal techniques to help children and adolescents to acquire appropriate behaviours. A useful approach to teaching children how to say 'No' and to resist negative influences is given below.

- Use a large sheet of paper and a texta to write down five to eight ways to say 'No'.
- Identify an issue,
  e.g. smoking at school,
  wagging a class, etc.
- Use a second sheet of paper to write down reasons to refuse to do one of the above.

n.b. When writing down these statements write them *how* they are to be said.

How to say 'No'	*Reasons not to wag*
• No thanks	• I'm already in trouble
• No way	• They might mark the roll
• I don't want to, you go ahead . . . but	• We might be seen
• Not for me, etc.	• I need the work, etc.

These sheets of paper are used as 'cue cards' and they are pinned up so the target student can see them.

Now the child is put under pressure with an offer such as: 'Hey, Tom, let's wag this period. Mr Jones is away and it's only a relief teacher who won't know we're missing.'

The child or adolescent then responds to this offer and to several more requests and pressuring statements to conform by using the cue cards, e.g. No way . . . I'm already in trouble, etc.

The two opposing sides — student under pressure and pressure group — continue until there is a clear halt to proceedings.

Broken Record

It is often important to sound like an old gramophone record stuck in a groove and repeating the same thing over and over again . . . and again . . . and again.

No thanks, you go ahead . . .
No thanks, you can if you want to . . .
No thanks, I really don't think it's a good idea . . .
No thanks, etc.

Once the target student has had sufficient opportunity to rehearse resistance, he or she should practise without the cue sheets. A range of negative peer-group-pressure problems should be discussed and those particularly relevant to each student should be selected to make the practice situations as realistic as possible.

UNIT 4 Organisational Checklists

Time required: 20–30 minutes
Format: 1:1 or group setting
Materials required: A blank card to write on.
At any stage in the program it is important to spend a short time in establishing whether each target student is correctly organised. The fact that it has not been mentioned until now does not imply that this exercise should be left until the final stage. It is suggested that the Organisational Checklist be established after three or four sessions and then repeatedly followed up during the entire program to ensure that the student's level of organisation has not fallen below par.

The student should be made aware of his or her responsibility regarding correct equipment and organisation. Many students get into trouble because they do not have their pens, pencils, books, etc. and they are invariably out of their seats borrowing items of equipment or asking for spare paper, etc. It is absolutely essential that high school students have the right books each day and they should have an up-to-date copy of their timetable. Students who lose books and are generally unorganised spend a large proportion of the school day engaged in off-task activities and all the good work regarding conflict skills will be of no avail if the relatively simple task of being organised is not attended to.

Making a Checklist

A checklist relevant to the specific setting should be prepared. High school children will require a more inclusive list than primary school children. An example of a checklist is given below but it should be noted that this list is not intended to be complete:

- timetable
- writing tools, e.g. pens and pencils
- an exercise book as required for each subject
- spare paper
- homework schedule
- P.E. equipment
- industrial arts, domestic science, technical drawing equipment as required
- ruler, eraser, textas
- a diary

The diary is most important as students should learn to write into it their organisation for the week. Each day should be listed, and books and equipment needed for that day should be indicated.

After the student has prepared the list, the teacher who is working with him or her should check to make sure that everything is there. Financial constraints could exist in some cases and it is important to be aware of these and to ask parents to help in getting their child organised. The parents are also in a position to inform teachers if problems should arise.

Additional Training

Many students find themselves in trouble for not listening and for wasting time. It may be helpful to employ some of the training approaches discussed in Section 5. Of particular value to conduct disordered students is the on-task training unit which focuses on the use of a plan, and of monitoring and cueing in some settings.

The teacher should be aware that there are no quick cures or magic approaches. It is a characteristic of adolescents, and particularly of students identified as conduct disordered, that they will not sustain energy for sufficiently long periods of time to complete all the work in this course. Adolescents and children who experience behaviour problems at school will usually work until they see an improvement in their position. When they are in less trouble and are no longer sent out of the class constantly, their motivation often lessens and they cease to keep up the levels of application required to stay out of trouble completely.

It is important to recognise the stop-start nature which often characterises an adolescent's approach to working on these issues. The expectations of other teachers and adults can be a problem if they believe that this program will change the 'artful dodger' into a perfectly behaved little 'angel'. It is quite customary for the target children to show considerable improvement but to slip back to some of their bad habits as motivation lessens. It is common to work for four or five weeks and then to stop and wait for another crisis to occur in order to re-engage the target student for a second or even third 'hit' with the program. The important point to bear in mind is the need to 'hang in' there with the student and not to give up too soon or to have expectations that improvement will be rapid and total. In many instances the second or even third 'application' of later parts of the program has produced greater gains, but not until several problems had been encountered.

Thus the message is clear: the program can help children and adolescents to gain greater control over their maladaptive behaviour but it cannot be expected to be the 'total' answer. Nor can this or any program be right for every child. It is important to recognise that some children may need approaches completely different from the Talk Sense to Yourself program. Despite these comments regarding the problems that are likely to be encountered, there is optimism that many students will gain from the units of work. The total picture is of course much wider and schools must also attend to the issues of staff development, conflict resolution skills, organisational and systems approaches, as well as to curriculum development.

4

Monitoring and Cueing for Behaviour Change

Monitoring

Many behaviour problems occurring in classrooms or less structured situations can be managed successfully by helping the student clearly to identify and recognise the problem.

When attention is directed towards specific behaviours, these behaviours can be changed. Before starting a monitoring, contracting or cueing system, it is important for the target child or target children to attend a meeting where the nature of the monitoring system will be explained. The value of monitoring systems used in schools is often reduced because students cannot obtain feedback about their progress. Students need to be given information regarding their level of progress in taking control over their behaviour. Most of the monitoring and cueing systems described will require the setting of behavioural targets in order to produce self-management and self-review in students. Monitoring and cueing systems can help students whose misbehaviour is so well entrenched that it is almost at an unconscious level. The variety of contracts, cueing and monitoring approaches can also be linked with certain contingencies such as sanctions, rewards, etc.

Monitoring and cueing approaches can be successfully tied to the Talk Sense to Yourself program where students set goals, make plans and generally try to self-guide in order to stop maladaptive behaviours and replace them with adaptive functioning.

Contracts and Daily Report Cards

Contracts or student/teacher agreements are the lowest and, generally speaking, the least efficient of the monitoring systems because usually no direct feedback is involved. As a rule, a set of target behaviours is defined and at the end of a day or a week the student is given feedback regarding success or lack of it. These contracts can be linked to parent/school coalitions as well as to sanctions and punishments. Agreements regarding behaviour are often written into daily report cards to take home to parents. But frequently the behaviours being targeted and the criteria by which they are to be judged are too diffuse. An agreement or contract could be reached between a student and a teacher along the following lines.

A contract system must begin by clearly establishing the nature of the behaviours. These behaviours must be specific, not general.

General Behaviours
- be polite
- try harder

- be well behaved
- have good manners
- behave properly, etc

Specific Behaviours
- do not argue with teachers
- follow instructions quickly
- stay in your seat — no walking around
- put up your hand — do not call out
- do not call names or swear, etc.

The contract must be taught to the student and he or she must learn it perfectly.

Many contracts are not internalised by a process of memorisation and are external to the student. It should take about three days to train the student so that he or she can accurately recall the contract. The contract should be started following the training procedure and it should run for between one and four weeks, depending on the age of the student. It should specify not only the behaviours to be stopped, but also the target behaviours to be established. It may include penalty or success clauses which clearly detail what will happen if the student fails or succeeds.

Example of a Student/Teacher Agreement

Behaviours to Stop	*Behaviours to Start*
• Calling out in class.	• Put hand up if something to say.
• Not doing what teacher asks.	• Follow instructions.
• Arguing with teacher.	• Accept teacher's decisions.
• Getting out of seat and wandering about.	• Remain in seat.

I .... will try to change my behaviours.
                   (student's name)

Date ....

FAILURE to stay under control will mean:
- Letter sent home telling parents you are in trouble.
- Not permitted in playground.

SUCCESS in sticking to the agreement will mean:
- Parents advised of good conduct.
- Use of computer for 30 minutes on Monday and Thursday during lunch hour.

Daily report cards can serve as extensions of the contract, because although the use of contracts can be of value, with a conduct disordered child it is often necessary to move to a more intense level of monitoring for behaviour change.

Many high schools use a daily report card which each student takes to each class. Often these report cards are badly designed. They lack specificity and objectivity and their reliability depends upon an individual teacher's interpretation of loose terms such as 'satisfactory', 'well behaved' or 'poorly behaved'.

Such report cards frequently produce dissension and anger in the student, and can be counterproductive. For example, a student who is trying hard not to argue, answer back or get into conflict with peers (this being his or her understanding of what behaving properly means) may give the daily report card to a teacher and have it marked 'unsatisfactory' because the teacher expected more work to be done and assignments to be handed in. This expectation by the teacher, whilst not unreasonable, was not part of the contract and as a result the student moves out of the lesson angry, frustrated, and possibly more disruptive.

It is therefore very important for teachers and students to have a correct understanding of contracts and daily report cards. Specific and agreed behaviours must be used in order to prevent misunderstandings. Counterproductive daily reporting systems have been the cause of further misbehaviour. The most common example occurs when teachers expect 100 per cent levels of improvement and are not prepared to accept misbehaviour of any kind from a conduct disordered child or adolescent. Behaviour rarely moves from a minus 10 to a plus 10 on a conduct scale and where gains occur they must be recognised, whilst deficit or problem behaviours in other areas will need work at a later stage. These comments can best be illustrated with an example from real life:

> Tony, a boy of 13, returned to school following a suspension. During the suspension he worked on elements of the Talk Sense to Yourself program. He had been suspended for non-compliance, hostile behaviour involving arguments with teachers, including threats, insults, rude gestures, and violence. He had pushed a teacher and run out of class leaving several chairs, boys and assorted items strewn across the floor in his wake. He returned to school and was placed on a loosely defined daily report card system. Four days later his report card was stamped as unsatisfactory by the teacher of one class because he had not completed all the set work and he had failed to bring the correct book. The boy became angry (as did the teacher), and was sent to the deputy, who threatened him with another suspension. The daily record card had been set up in relation to behaviour in the classroom and the fact that Tony did not have a particular book became the focus on which the teacher judged the boy's behaviour in class. To the boy's credit, he managed to control his temper. However, the unspecified behaviour becoming the target for the teacher's criticism highlights the problems of interpretation.

To sum up, then, the daily report card is a valuable and flexible tool for use in schools in developing agreed-upon target behaviours, but it must be objective, specific and, above all, internalised through memorisation.

It is not the object of the daily report card to keep a catalogue of offences but rather to serve as a feedback and awareness-producing system which makes students cognisant of behaviours considered to be problems. Specific comments, verbal or written on the card, should always be given so that the student has a clear idea of progress. In order to improve its value the daily report system can be used with the approaches of tallies, monitoring and cueing.

The system of tallying specific behaviours is extremely valuable both in primary and high schools and can be used with or without contracts and daily report cards. Its major aim is to try to produce awareness of specific behaviours which are causing problems. Many of these behaviours occur so frequently that they are almost at a subconscious level. Wasting time, talking, calling out, being out of the seat, arguing, etc. all fit into this category. Children who are very disruptive are usually unaware of the effect their behaviour has on others; they are only concerned about having their needs met and so they are poorly controlled and egocentric. It may be necessary to shape the required behaviour by using both tallying and cueing approaches.

Setting up the System of Monitoring and Cueing

After a lesson, time should be set aside for discussion regarding the problem behaviours. During this time the teacher should propose a tallying or even a cueing system. The target child should be clearly informed of the nature of the cues or tallies that will be kept. It will normally be necessary to set up a system which permits the child to obtain immediate feedback as the tally score increases. The approaches outlined in this section can all be used in such a way that the target child can see the score or the tally as it occurs. At the end of a lesson the teacher should then discuss its progress with the child.

Monitoring and cueing systems can be used with groups of misbehaving students in much the same way. Once a private discussion after class has taken place in which the monitoring system has been set up, the tally will reflect the behaviour of the group. If only one or two members of the group cause the problems, the monitoring system is renegotiated in relation to the offenders. Scores may also be linked to consequences and the offending child or group can be given a maximum score which can be accumulated before a punishment previously agreed upon is given.

Tallying

Tallying is basically defined as observing and keeping score of a specific behaviour or group of behaviours. It is often employed to bring to awareness specific problems and this is done with the full knowledge of the child. It is very important that the child be made aware that the teacher is keeping a tally of the defined behaviours. If the child or adolescent is aware of being observed and recorded, many of the problem behaviours are inhibited; clearly this is the required spin-off. Awareness produces change and with the increased level of awareness directed at specific behaviours, these behaviours can be brought under conscious control.

Example of a Tally Card

I saw you talking on 12 occasions in the last lesson	Tally kept on John when talking
	<u>XXXX XXXX</u> <u>XXXX</u>

If a child has a chart of behaviours, the tallies can be recorded and a target set for the next session. A counsellor or teacher can set a target 25 to 50 per cent below the previous level of disruptive outbursts and then the child can be given a specific target maximum to be aimed for.

> 'Last time you called out 12 times. Now I will keep a tally next time so let's see if you can reduce this to a maximum of 6 times, or less.'

Keeping the Tally in View of the Target Child

If the tallying system is organised in such a way that the target child cannot see the score, this will be less effective than keeping a record which is in the child's view. The problem of how to provide a display giving immediate feedback without making the whole class aware can be overcome. If the adolescent or child is seated close to the teacher's desk, it should be possible to tally on a piece of card positioned at the edge of the desk. The tally must be large enough to be seen at a distance of two metres and although several others in the front row can also see it there is no reason why they need to know its purpose even if they ask.

Another simple tallying device is to use a couple of containers in which pens and pencils are stored. Teachers' desks normally have a variety of such objects lying about and they do not usually arouse suspicion. The tallying occurs as the target child sees the pencils being removed and either placed in another container or disappear into the desk drawer. This very concrete example can also be linked to cueing, explained later in this section. The concept of disappearing pencils can be linked to losing chances:

> 'Like a cat, you have seven lives and each time you see a pencil disappear that's one life gone. If you lose all seven, the consequences are . . .'

In fact an endless number of systems can be employed to let a student know his or her progress. A pile of books could be used instead of the pencils, or a book or marker that can be moved along the length of a table or cupboard from one end to the other to indicate an increased score. The variations depend on the available space, furniture and ingenuity of the teacher.

Cueing

Many behaviours causing concern in structured and unstructured situations are almost at the subconscious level of responding. Children call out or display poor attention spans, shout or hit as part of a fixed pattern of behavioural responses. These behaviours are so much a part of the particular child's repertoire that they have become habits and quite often tallying or matching cannot be easily achieved as the child is unaware of the undesirable behaviour. In such cases it will be necessary to use a cueing approach. Most situations permit the employment of both tallies/matching and cueing systems in order to produce behaviour change.

In some circumstances tallying may be done in a more public way without producing problems. It has been pointed out to classes that sometimes the teacher will monitor a particular situation by keeping a score on the corner of the board. The purpose of monitoring and the particular method used may be explained but the children are not told who the target or targets may be. Sometimes they know, but the identity is hardly ever indicated unless the whole class is being monitored. This can be successful too. A spin-off often occurs because the members of the class

CUEING

GOOD | NOT SO GOOD | TROUBLE

BOOK MOVED ALONG BENCH GIVES
STUDENT FEEDBACK

CUEING

TALLYING

are aware that monitoring is taking place; some children wonder whether they are under the microscope, being monitored. If this belief prevails the children often work much harder and try to behave correctly and thus the class benefits.

Small groups can be monitored in the same way as individuals. Once again, in an interview the offending group of children is told that monitoring will take place. Goals are set and the group is made aware of each member's responsibility to ensure that it is not his or her behaviour which causes the rest of the group to suffer. Where the group is clearly led or influenced by one member, the monitoring system reverts to that child as the individual target.

A cue is a signal used to let a child know that he or she is engaged in a specified inappropriate behaviour. The cue is meant to be a focus for the target child only and should be used by the teacher as a 'secret' signal so that cueing becomes private. The other members of the group are aware that a child is being cued and this is usually not a problem.

Cueing can be approached in various ways.

A special object such as a tennis ball or a particular book may be used. The object is picked up by the teacher who holds it for 30 seconds and moves close enough to the student so that the signal can be seen. The student should then bring the behaviour under control.

Tallying and cueing to teach awareness and self-correction are often used together. One example of combining the two approaches is to use the pencils-in-the-container tallying system with a cueing approach. The pencil is taken out of the container and the teacher makes sure that the target child sees it. If the child immediately returns to his or her task and stops the misbehaviour the teacher replaces the pencil in the original container. The target student therefore does not lose a 'life' unless he or she ignores the cue.

Another approach is to use a flip-over coloured-card system. This card set should have three colours. Red for danger — you are off task; orange for approaching danger — watch out; and green for no problems. These 'traffic lights' are turned over so that the appropriate one is showing.

In some schools magnetic boards with a red dot that goes up or down depending on whether child is on task or off task have been used.

A humorous approach is to play 'Hangman' on a small section of the board or on a piece of paper. This is a tallying device where the child can see that he or she is going the right way to get 'hanged' and it is amazing how effective this can be, especially when the noose appears.

In circumstances where a child is not attending to stimuli displayed at the front of the class, a variety of other cues can be used, such as

- walking up to the child and tapping on its shoulder or its desk.
- using a short sharp sound such as is made by tapping a pencil on a desk.
- throwing a ball casually from hand to hand in front of the target child or placing the ball on the child's desk for a moment. (This can be very useful, especially if the class is accustomed to seeing the teacher with a ball in hand.)

Any number of alternatives can be used depending on available materials and the teacher's ingenuity.

5

On-Task Training for Attention Deficit Disorders and Hyperactivity

This section focuses on a cognitive behavioural approach to helping children with attention deficit disorders and hyperactivity to gain greater control of their impulsive, uncontrolled and disorganised behaviour.

The nature of these disorders and their treatment was discussed in Section 1. Counsellors or teachers who wish to implement the on-task training program with individual children or whole classes should consult Section 1 in order to focus more specifically on the philosophy and research findings which underpin this program.

A Cognitive Behavioural Approach

The program outlined below has been successfully used in a range of educational settings. The on-task training units can be applied to a whole-class environment, a small group, or an individual. In most classrooms there are two or three children who can be identified as attention deficit disordered and these children will need special small-group training in addition to the normal program implemented in the classroom.

The best way to introduce the program in a class setting is first to identify the two or more target students who will require most training. Their training should begin in a small group ahead of the rest of the class. Alternatively, on-task training can begin with the whole class and the identified target students can subsequently be withdrawn for several sessions of extra training. The procedures outlined below will be the same for small groups and for whole classes but clearly the purpose of small-group work is to provide the additional training required.

Before training begins, the issue of compliance must be dealt with. Any serious problems regarding the target child or children's compliance will have to be addressed. Most children will follow the teacher's instructions but some children may require specific compliance training so that the on-task training unit will have maximum effect. The combination of compliance training and on-task training has proved to be a reasonably effective approach.

Before starting the program, the points outlined in Table 7 should be considered.

Table 7   Improving Efficacy in Relation to On-Task (SIT) Training

---

- Teach skills to mastery wherever possible. Thus do not allocate a specified number of lessons to units but run each skill step for sufficient time to permit mastery to be attained.
- Teach skills under strictly controlled conditions. Do not allow children to become disruptive or the training time will degenerate into a 'who's in control' unit.
- Plan for a series of sessions.
- Give target children clear and accurate feedback regarding progress.
- Provide both individual and small-group instruction where possible.
- Use a variety of charts or stickers, etc. to help to improve motivation.
- Consider compliance training for children who do not follow instructions.

On-task training has been successfully used in infants, primary and high schools. It is particularly useful in slower-learner classes where on-task behaviour is more needed yet is often absent. On-task training has been used at the beginning of a school year or term to promote organisational efficiency and enhance future learning and engagement time. It has also been used where classes are experiencing work-related problems, either with the whole class or with special target individuals who would benefit most by its application.

Cueing and Monitoring as an Adjunct to On-Task Training

As previously mentioned, compliance training and on-task training can be complementary to each other. In Section 4 cueing and monitoring were dealt with in relation to helping a conduct disordered child to bring specific aspects of his or her behaviour under control and the same skills can equally be applied to self-regulation of on-task behaviour. Section 4 should be reread to have a clear understanding of the methods which can be employed by teachers trying to cue an individual to take control of a specific behaviour.

It is important to explain to the target student what is expected of him or her. Enlist the student's co-operation in this endeavour. Most children are happy that the teacher is prepared to take the trouble to help them 'to take control' and improve their on-task behaviour. The target student can be allowed to choose the particular cueing or monitoring device if this will help to obtain voluntary co-operation. The cueing and monitoring approaches mentioned in Section 4 will provide the basis for the approach and the target behaviour or behaviours should be carefully identified and then learnt (to mastery) by the student.

Beginning the Program: Organisational Considerations

Target Children Identification

Decide which children (two or three) will require small-group training and start with these children for the first two or three sessions. Then begin to teach the rest of the class so that specific target children will obtain success due to their extra training time.

As the rest of the class catches up continue to give the most needy children extra sessions.

Consider using an on-task unit each day for ten days to build up awareness and therefore plan ahead by preparing any materials required well in advance.

Integration of the Three Main Components of On-Task Training

Figure 6 shows the framework for on-task training. Three major components need to be integrated during the training stages. The first to be introduced is 'the plan'. Depending on the age of the child, the plan may have two, three or even four stages which teach the child to direct attention and to remain 'on task' as the full model is built up. As the plan progresses the second component is added to the model and the target child is taught to self-instruct by first observing an adult model and then proceeding to overt and covert self-instruction. The third component is the provision of distraction factors. The target children are taught to resist the distraction caused by 'pests or blockers' who attempt to interfere with the completion of several tasks.

The total model incorporates these three elements and each set of skills is integrated by teaching and practice into the overall framework.

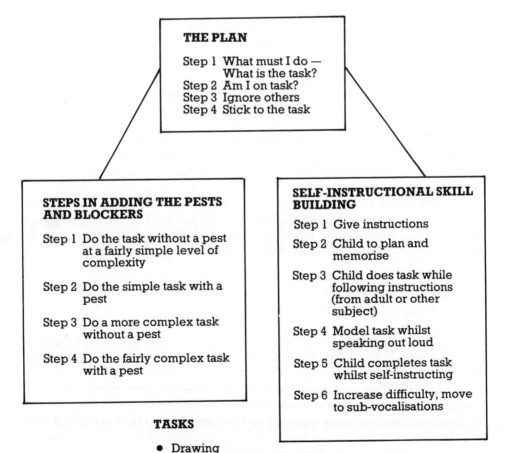

THE PLAN

Step 1 What must I do —
        What is the task?
Step 2 Am I on task?
Step 3 Ignore others
Step 4 Stick to the task

STEPS IN ADDING THE PESTS AND BLOCKERS

Step 1 Do the task without a pest at a fairly simple level of complexity

Step 2 Do the simple task with a pest

Step 3 Do a more complex task without a pest

Step 4 Do the fairly complex task with a pest

SELF-INSTRUCTIONAL SKILL BUILDING

Step 1 Give instructions

Step 2 Child to plan and memorise

Step 3 Child does task while following instructions (from adult or other subject)

Step 4 Model task whilst speaking out loud

Step 5 Child completes task whilst self-instructing

Step 6 Increase difficulty, move to sub-vocalisations

TASKS
- Drawing
- Copying
- Following instructions
- Roving commissions, etc.

Figure 6 **On-Task Training Program**

Lesson Units

Time required: Approximately ten sessions will be required to teach the skills of on-task training. No set time can be allocated to the unit as this will depend on the level of training needed for each group or class. Teachers should decide how much time to set aside for each training session.

Format: Group or whole-class setting

Materials required: A large copy of the plan, children's copies of the plan, various mazes, codes, pen and pencil tasks, as well as a variety of materials such as books, pens, rulers, etc.

A plan can be used with children from early school age (six or seven years) up to late adolescence. It can be elaborated upon or reduced depending on the nature of the task and the age of the child. Once a specific plan has been decided upon, it should be taught by starting with the first line and then introducing each successive line in turn until the full three-stage model is reached.

The self-guiding plan should first be written in large print on to a poster-size piece of cardboard which can easily be read by a child from the back of the classroom. The poster should be made in such a way that each line can be covered up to permit specific focusing on a selected line or lines. In addition, a copy of the plan that can be attached to his or her book or to the desk should be made by each student; normally postcard size is sufficient for these.

Each plan may reflect the specific needs of the child and the essential elements of the case. In the earlier Talk Sense to Yourself approaches simple plans were made which involved children and adolescents in focus questions and self-statements such as:

> Is what I'm doing helping me?
> Talk sense to myself.
> Give myself good advice, etc.

In reducing the complexity of the plan the teacher will have to decide precisely which elements are most relevant to the particular child and incorporate these accordingly. There is no one plan or one set of goal-directed instructions which is absolutely essential and quite often the child begins to substitute its own phrases or add or subtract lines to suit its personal constructs. In working with different children across a range of settings it is important to be flexible and to permit the child to change the surface structures as long as the deep meaning is still kept.

Plans can therefore be made for a variety of situations in relation to attention deficits as well as to conduct disorders and problem-solving situations.

EXAMPLES OF A PLAN

PLAN

1 What is my task?

2 Am I on task?

3 Ignore others.

4 Stick to my task and finish it.

PLAN (simplified)

1 What do I have to do?

2 Am I doing it?

3 How am I going?

PLAN (reduced in complexity)

1 What is the task?	or	1 What is my task?
2 Am I on task?		2 Am I on task?
3 Finish the task.		

The Plan

Initially, the first line of the plan is taught and the other lines are covered up. This line should be used in conjunction with a variety of situations which demand a clear sequence of movements around a room. These tasks are referred to as commissions and they may differ in complexity and length relative to the developmental level of the target child. Even if the child cannot read, the card is used as a cue sheet and a sufficient amount of rehearsal is given so that the task may be learnt.

The Commissions

The commissions involve children in carrying out between two and five specific tasks given in a set sequence.

> put that book under the chair
> then close the door
> then switch on the light
> > (3 commissions)

or

> move the chair under the table
> open the book on the table to page 14
> then note the first three words at the top of page 14
> now go to the blackboard and write down the words
> finally close the book and sit down
> > (5 commissions)

or

> go to the table and pick up all the red pencils
> (about 15 pencils of different colours are placed there)
> put all the red pencils on the tray
> (2 commissions)

Different tasks can be used to teach the target children to direct their attention towards accurate recall.

Mazes and codes. A simple maze can be constructed and codes can also be used.

Writing or copying tasks. Writing down the alphabet and then working out a child's name in numbers which correspond to the letters of the alphabet, or copying down a sentence and checking for accuracy are ideal tasks.

Counting aloud. Tasks such as counting backwards from twenty or forwards in fours or backwards in threes, etc. can be included. Once again the complexity of the task will be determined by the levels of development in the child.

Searching (and substituting). A passage can be given with the instructions that a certain target word is to be underlined each time it occurs. This can also be done with numbers and the complexity of the task can be increased to include two, three or even four words to be underlined. In addition, one or more of the target words can be substituted for other words. It is best to use words fairly similar in meaning, e.g. rich for wealthy, the for a, etc.

Drawing tasks. These are usually timed tasks set for two, three, four or more minutes, during which time the child must continue to draw the specified object; a house, a man, etc.

The nature of the tasks is limited only by the degree of ingenuity the teacher possesses. There is no reason why novel tasks cannot be presented but wherever possible they should reflect real situations and especially those in which the child is having some difficulty (e.g. academic ones).

The first step of the plan focuses on teaching the child to remember the task and to learn to follow instructions, thus before the child is permitted to move around the room the instructions should be repeated aloud and corrections, if any, made. Once the instructions are clear, the steps of self-instructional skill building are applied, as outlined in Figure 6.

Integrating the Three Elements of the Program

Level 1

At this level the target child is taught to attend to instructions given in relation to step 1 of the plan.

(a) Child asks itself (aloud): 'What is the task?' or 'What do I have to do?'. (b) Child then answers (aloud): 'I have to put the pen on the table, then I have to take the book from the chair and put it on my desk open at page 23.'

Level 2

At this level the self-instructional training sequence identified in Figure 6 is followed.

Step 1: Adult gives instructions.

Step 2: Child memorises instructions and plans for the task.

Step 3: Child does task while following instructions from teacher (or from another member of the training group).

Step 4: Adult models task while self-instructing aloud.

Step 5: Child completes task while self-instructing aloud.

Step 6: Child completes more difficult task while self-instructing subvocally.

It is normal to use several sets of different instructions during these training phases.

Level 3

At this point the distraction stages are added by introducing 'pests or blockers'. If several children are involved in the program they alternate as 'pests or blockers' and as subjects who are trying to self-instruct and remain on task.

Before moving to the distraction stages, steps 2, 3, and 4 of the plan are added.

Step 2: Am I on task?

Step 3: Ignore others.

Step 4: Stick to the task

These steps can be simplified for younger children, e.g. 'ignore others and stay on task'.

The job of a pest or blocker is to distract the target child from completing the task. The pest is not allowed to interfere physically with the on-task child but should talk to it and try to distract it from the task that is under way. The pest can ask questions of the on-task child, move into its way (blocking) and generally act like a pest.

Pest or blockers are added in the following steps:

Step 1: The task is done at a fairly simple level without a pest.

Step 2: The simple task is done with a pest or blocker present and interfering.

Step 3: A more complex task is done without a pest or blocker.

Step 4: The complex task is done with a pest or blocker present and interfering.

During the development of the steps the target child is taught not only to employ the self-instructional directives but also to integrate the relevant steps of the plan:

Teacher asks the child to describe the plan after first giving instructions, 'What is your plan?'

Child answers, 'The task I have to do is to open this book at page 23

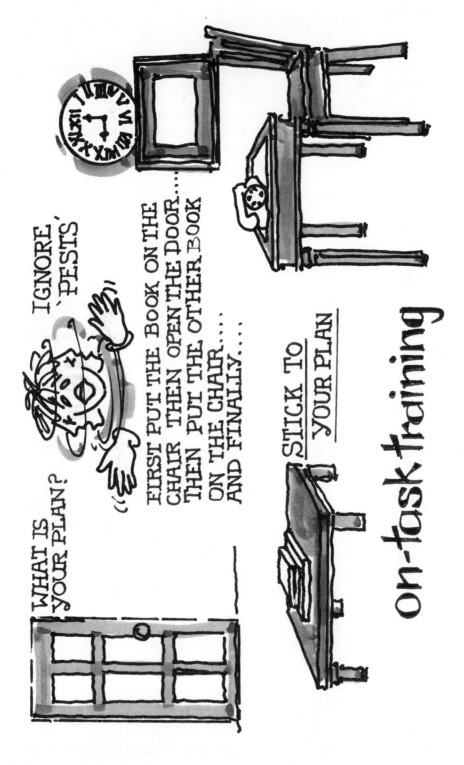

IGNORE 'PESTS'

WHAT IS YOUR PLAN?

FIRST PUT THE BOOK ON THE CHAIR THEN OPEN THE DOOR.... THEN PUT THE OTHER BOOK ON THE CHAIR...... AND FINALLY.....

STICK TO YOUR PLAN

On-task training

and begin to copy the first five lines. I must remain on task and ignore others. When I have finished copying out the five lines I will draw a picture about the story. I must stick to my plan.'

The above example illustrates how the elements of the plan and the instructions are integrated. In teaching the target child to develop these integrated skills it will be necessary to work in a part/whole approach which builds up on each successive step towards a complete integration of the plan and the instructions. Some children will not be able to combine successfully the various elements of the plan while others find little difficulty. When working with slower children it will be necessary to modify the instructions and to shorten the plan; expectations will also have to be modified and approximations towards a goal accepted.

Vocabulary and Concept Development

When training in on-task behaviour begins, most children do not fully understand such terms as 'on task' or 'off task' or what a plan is; younger children might also have difficulty working out what 'ignoring pests and blockers' means. The training steps develop these concepts and a specific vocabulary which at the conclusion of the program become clear reference points for children to assess their performance and to guide or regulate current and future behaviour.

Timed Tasks

After the basic elements of the self-instructional model have been learnt, the use of timed tasks in which the target child learns to follow a plan for a set length of time is important. The research of Douglas and Peters (1979) pointed to the problem ADD-H children have in relation to sustained attention, and the object of timed tasks is to develop and expand the ability to persevere with set tasks.

The two pieces of equipment required for timed tasks are an egg timer and a clock. The best kind of clock is one with a face which the child can see clearly and which is also large enough for the individual minutes to be seen. Kitchen timers can be used where the minutes are set and a bell rings after a countdown. A photographic clock or a digital clock can also be useful and towards the end of the training sessions the child should be encouraged to use its own watch.

Various tasks lend themselves to being timed and selection depends on the age and ability of the child. During the timed task some interruptions which tempt the child to become distracted can be scheduled.

Examples of Some Timed Tasks

- draw a man, a house, a ship
- work on a puzzle, a crossword, a jigsaw
- write a story on a given topic
- copy text from a book
- work on a maths sheet
- read a book

Instructions would be given so that the child understands that when drawing, for example, pictures should be elaborated rather than regarded as finished. Curtains, paths, flowers, bricks, etc. can be added to a house until the time is up!

Small tasks and brief working times should be set at first. These are best accomplished with the aid of the egg timer with its very concrete display. After some progress, the switch to clocks or other timers can be made.

Note that it is better to have three or four on-task periods of eight to ten minutes rather than attempt to go for huge, unattainable chunks.

Working with the Whole Class

Once work is under way with the selected target children who require extra training due to their high levels of inattentiveness, the program can be started with the rest of the class. The steps are similar, except that the opportunity to engage in tasks requiring movement around the room (such as the commissions) is significantly reduced and more academically or transition-based tasks are substituted.

The number of lesson units is related to mastery and available time allocation; the program should be flexible. The set of activities depends on the ages of the children and the following example is for nine- to ten-year-olds.

(a) Introduce the plan and get each child to copy it on to a card.
(b) Use the alphabet-code task to teach the basics of the first step of the plan. Repeat this step with a variety of precise instructions, e.g. draw an 8-centimetre square and inside it write the first two lines of the plan in number code, etc.
(c) Introduce the next parts of the plan with several of the tasks of counting backwards in twos or threes, and begin to use blockers or pests.
(d) Incorporate the self-instructional components of the plan, using commissions, and then select two or three children to demonstrate. Do this several times with different children and build up the numbers until six to eight children are moving around the classroom at any one time, including two or three blockers. Children not involved in the commissions should be taught to remain on task by being given the job of mentally following the 'performers' and observing their actions to determine whether the set tasks are followed in the correct sequence. A variety of semi-academic or school-based tasks can be set which closely resemble classroom life. You could, for example, instruct the children to: 'collect your writing books, then take out your maths books and do only the first six sums. Then start writing the story about a TV show until the wall clock says 11.45. Remember to stay on task and ignore others'.
(e) Use a number of timed tasks during which you will move around the class cueing four or five children to act as pests for one minute and then return to their on-task activity, while you cue other children with a gentle tap on the back or in some other subtle way.

Motivation

A variety of simple charts can be employed to encourage target children to develop the skills of sustained attention and on-task behaviour. These charts would be drawn up to show the number of times each child successfully completes a task, or to show with a bar graph the number of minutes a task has been sustained. Target lines or specific totals could be tied into a reward system, such as stickers, free play with a game, or computer time.

Compliance Training

The on-task training program clearly requires, and to some degree develops, compliance in the target children. However, some children require additional compliance training in order to develop skills of sustained attention. The following ideas are designed to promote compliance skills in such children. These suggestions are not intended as a substantive unit in the development of compliance. If necessary, a special program to resolve this issue will have to be formulated before proceeding to self-instructional training.

Simon Says

A simple and non-threatening method is to start off with 'Simon says' or 'O'Grady says'. Most children have played and enjoyed these games. The game should progress from the idea of only doing a task when 'Simon says' to the stage where it is played without reference to a specific name. A method of generalising compliance away from 'Simon' is to play the game from a chair or some other specified position such as beside the window, or when the teacher touches the children's desk. In this way the children are cued to obey instructions from various positions around a room. Finally, the importance of following instructions when the teacher merely faces the individual or group is stressed, and at this stage it is necessary to move into timed and recorded tasks.

Improving Response Time and Error Rate

When working with a small group or class, the names of the children are put on a board or written on a large sheet of paper and then each child can obtain feedback in terms of a progress score. The object in this game is to try to speed up the level of responses and to make responding as automatic as possible.

```
          RESPONSE TIME — 5 SECONDS
          NUMBER OF ERRORS

          JOHN              XXX
          SALLY             X
          TIM               XX
```

The game is linked to the attempt to follow a set of instructions which are given as separate commands. The target children have to respond within a given time of between three and six seconds.

Example of an Instruction Set

- pick up your pencil
- draw a picture of a man
- put down your pencil and fold your arms
- open your book to page 34
- stand up
- sit down
- close your book and put all your equipment in the box
- get out six pencils and two pens from the case
- write your first name at the top right corner of the page
- stop work and collect those books from that table

Each of the instructions on the list is given separately and at different levels of pacing and loudness so that the children can't anticipate. Many of these instructions are related to school-based tasks because so many ADD-H children have difficulty in educational settings.

Nature of Teacher Instructions

In a compliance unit there must be no ambiguity or changes in the instruction set. Instructions should be given as clearly and concisely as possible and they should contain an imperative: 'Put away your books . . . now.'

If the instruction is repeated, it is important to keep it identical or as close to the original as possible. Teachers should not be drawn into a speech about children 'not listening' or make additional comments which change the instruction set. Simply repeat, louder and with added emphasis: 'Put away your books . . . NOW.'

Mistakes can easily be made in teaching children compliance and a few such errors are listed below.

- making the instructional command too much like a comment
- changing the repeat command to something which may be similar in 'deep' meaning to what has been said but is quite different at the structural level: original — 'sit up and look at me'; repeat — 'the class just does not listen; now I expect you all to stop what you are doing and to look this way and pay attention.'
- starting a new instruction before 100 per cent compliance is achieved
- leaving the room or attending to another issue before the original task is well under way
- letting the learner do something different from what is instructed or letting the learner leave the room or situation before the task is completed

Once the teacher in control of the session is clear about the concise and direct manner in which instructional commands are to be given, a set of approximately a dozen instructions should be worked out and then the training unit should continue.

The response time should be set at five seconds, and participating students informed of this, so that they can respond within the set time.

The previously devised instruction set is now given to the group or class and feedback is provided with a chart which, if appropriate, is marked to indicate that a child was too slow. The set is given at least three or four times in order to establish compliance and speed. If the first set of instructions is successful, a second set can be worked out to develop the level of responding further.

Generalisation can be achieved over time by continuing to integrate the on-task and compliance strategies into normal lessons and by teaching students to apply plans and ignore 'pests' through brief exercise sessions during the week. In addition, cueing and monitoring strategies can be employed with selected students to increase awareness and further develop skills usage.

References

American Psychiatric Association (1980). *Diagnostic statistical manual of mental disorders.* (3rd Ed.). Washington DC: APA.

Bandura, A. (1973). *Aggression: A social learning analysis.* Englewood Cliffs, New Jersey: Prentice-Hall.

Bornstein, M., Bellack, A. & Hersen, M. (1980). Social skills training for highly aggressive children. *Behaviour Modification, 4*, 173-186.

Bradshaw, K. (1987). Behaviour disordered children — To integrate or not. *Australian Journal of Remedial Education, 19* (1), 19-21.

Camp, B., Blom, G., Herbert, F. & van Doorninck, W. (1976). 'Think Aloud': A program for developing self-control in young aggressive boys. *Unpublished manuscript.* USA: University of Colorado School of Medicine.

Comber, L.C. & Whitfield, R.C. (1979). Action on indiscipline: A practical guide for teachers. In N. Frude, & H. Gault (Eds) (1984). *Disruptive behaviour in schools.* Chichester: John Wiley and Sons.

Copeland, P. (1983). Children's talking to themselves: its developmental significance, function and therapeutic promise. In P.C. Kendall (Ed.) *Advances in cognitive-behavioural research and therapy, 2.* New York: Academic Press.

Dodge, K.A. (1985). Attributional bias in aggressive children. In P.C. Kendall (Ed.) *Advances in cognitive behavioural research and therapy. 4.* Orlando, Florida: Academic Press, Inc.

Douglas, V. & Peters, K. (1979). Toward a clearer definition of the attentional deficits of hyperactive children. In G. Hale & M. Lewis (Eds), *Attention and the development of cognitive skills.* New York: Plenum Press.

Ellis, A. (1962). *Reason and emotion in psychotherapy.* New York: Stuart.

Feshbach, N.D. (1979). Empathy training: A field study in affective education. In S. Feshbach & A. Fraczek (Eds), *Aggression and behaviour change.* New York: Praeger.

Frude, N. & Gault, H. (1984). *Disruptive behaviour in schools.* Chichester: John Wiley and Sons.

Galloway, D., Ball, T., Blomfield, D. & Seyd, R. (1982). *Schools and disruptive pupils.* London: Longman.

Golden, G.S., (1980). Nonstandard therapies in the developmental disabilities. *American Journal of Diseases in Children, 134*:487.

Grimm, J., Bijou, S. & Parsons, J. (1978). A problem-solving model for teaching remedial arithmetic to handicapped young children. *Journal of Abnormal Child Psychology, 7*, 26-39.

Harner, I.C. & Foiles, R.A.L. (1980). Effect of Feingold's K-P diet on a residential, mentally handicapped population. *Journal American Dietetic Association.* 76-576.

Harris, K.R. (1986). The effects of cognitive behaviour modification on private speech and task performance during problem solving among learning-disabled and normally achieving children. *Journal of Abnormal Child Psychology, 14* (1), 63-67.

Hawkins, G. (1982). *Resistances to schools.* Sydney: Inner City Education Centre.

Hyde, N. & Robson, G. (1980). A study of student suspensions. In Western Australian Department of Education (1985), *Disruptive behaviour in schools.* Perth, W.A.: Ministerial Working Party Report.

Kendall, P.C. & Finch, A.J. (1978). A cognitive behavioural treatment for impulsivity: A group comparison study. *Journal of Consulting and Clinical Psychology, 48*, 80-91.

Kennedy, R.E. (1982). A cognitive-behavioural approach to the modification of aggressive behaviour in children. *School Psychology Review, 11*, 47-55.

Kettlewell, P.W. & Kausch, D.F. (1983). The generalisation of the effects of a cognitive-behavioural treatment program for aggressive children. *Journal of Abnormal Child Psychology, 11* (1), 101-114.

Kohlberg, L., Yaeger, J. & Hjertholm, E. (1968). Private speech: Four studies and a review of theories. *Child Development, 39*, 691-736.

Kupersmidt, J.B. (1983). Predicting delinquency and academic problems from childhood peer status. Paper presented at Symposium on Strategies for Identifying Children at Social Risk. In Kendall, P.C. (1985). *Cognitive-behavioural research and therapy*, **4,** New York: Academic Press Inc.

Lawrence, J., Steed, D. & Young, P. (1984). *Disruptive children — disruptive schools?* London: Croom Helm.

Lomax, R.G. & Cooley, W.W. (1979). *The student achievement instructional time relationship.* Paper presented at annual meeting of the American Educational Research Association, San Francisco.

Luria, A.R. (1961). *The role of speech in the regulation of normal and abnormal behaviour* (J. Tizard, trans.). New York: Liveright.

Meichenbaum, D. (1977). *Cognitive behaviour modification: An integrative approach.* New York: Plenum Press.

Meichenbaum, D. & Asarnow, J. (1979). Cognitive behavioural modification and metacognitive development: Implications for the classroom. In P.C. Kendall & S.D. Hollon (Eds). *Cognitive behavioural interventions: Theory, research and procedures.* New York: Academic Press.

Meichenbaum, D. & Goodman, J. (1971). Training impulsive children to talk to themselves. *Journal of Abnormal Psychology*, **77,** 115-126.

Meyers, A.W. & Cohen, R. (1984). Cognitive-behavioural interventions in educational settings. In P.C. Kendall *Advances in cognitive-behavioural research and therapy*, **3.** Florida: Academic Press Inc.

Nashby, W., Hayden, B. & DePaulo, B.M. (1980). Attributional bias among aggressive boys to interpret unambiguous social stimuli as displays of hostility. *Journal of Abnormal Psychology*, **89,** 459-468.

New South Wales Department of Education (1980). *Self discipline and pastoral care.* A report of the committee of enquiry into pupil behaviour and discipline in schools. Sydney: NSW Education Department.

Novaco, R.W. (1978). Anger and coping with stress. In J. Foreyt & D. Rathjen (Eds), *Cognitive behaviour therapy: Therapy, research and practice.* New York: Plenum Press.

Olweus, D. (1979). Stability of aggressive reaction patterns in males: A review. *Psychology Bulletin*, **86,** 852-872.

Palkes, H., Stewart, M. & Freedman, J. (1972). Improvement in maze performance on hyperactive boys as a function of verbal training procedures. *Journal of Special Education*, **5,** 337-342.

Rieth, H.J., Polsgrove, L. & Semmel, M.I. (1981). Instructional variables that make a difference: attention to task and beyond. *Exceptional Education Quarterly*, **2,** (3), 61-71.

Rosenshine, B.V. (1980). How time is spent in elementary classrooms. In D.C. Denham & A. Lieberman (Eds), *Time to learn.* Washington, DC: National Institute of Education.

Rossiter, A. (1983). The difficult-to-teach junior pupil. *SET research information for teachers,* Hawthorn, Victoria: ACER.

Rubel, R.J. (1977). *The unruly school: Disorders, disruptions and crimes.* Lexington: Heath and Company.

Rutter, M., Maughan B., Mortimore, P. & Ouston, J. (1979). *Fifteen thousand hours,* London: Open Books.

Safer, D.J. & Allen, R.P. (1976). *Hyperactive children: Diagnosis and management.* Baltimore: University Park Press.

Spivack, G. & Shure, M. (1974). *Social adjustment of young children: A cognitive approach to solving real-life problems.* San Francisco: Jossey-Bass.

Sprague, R.L. & Sleator, E.K. (1977). Methylphenidate in hyperkinetic children: Differences in dose effects on learning and social behaviour. *Science*, 198:1274.

Stallings, J., Needels, M. & Staybrook, N. (1979). *The teaching of basic reading skills in secondary schools, phase II and phase III,* Menlo Park, California: SRI International.

Torgensen, J.K. (1977). Memorization processes in reading disabled children. *Journal of Educational Psychology*, **69,** 571-578.

Torgensen, J.K. & Goldman, T. (1977). Rehearsal and short-term memory in second grade reading disabled children. *Child Development*, **48,** 56-61.

Torgensen, J.K. (1981). The relationship between memory and attention in learning disorders. *Exceptional Education Quarterly*, **2** (3), 51-59.

Urbain, E.S. & Kendall, P.C. (1980). Review of social-cognitive problem-solving interventions with children. *Psychological Bulletin*, **88,** 109-143.

Vygotsky, L.S. (1962). In E. Hanfmann & G. Vakar (Eds and trans.). *Thought and language.* Cambridge, Massachusetts: MIT Press (originally published 1934).

Walker, H.M. (1984). The current status of classification, assessment programming and service delivery issues relating to children with externalising behaviour disorders in the school setting. *The Australian Journal of Special Education,* **8** (2), 25-29.

Weiss, B., Williams, J.H., Margen, S., et al. (1980). Behavioural responses to artificial food colors. *Science,* 207-1487.

Western Australian Department of Education (1985). *Disruptive behaviour in schools.* Perth, W.A.: Ministerial working party report.

Whalen, C.K. & Henker, B. (1980). The social ecology of psycho-stimulant treatment: A model for conceptual and empirical analysis. In C.K. Whalen and B. Henker (Eds): *Hyperactive children: The social ecology of identification and treatment.* New York: Academic Press.

Whalen, C.K. & Henker, B. (1984). Hyperactivity and the attention deficit disorders: Expanding frontiers. *The Paediatric Clinics of North America,* **2** (3), 397-427.

Ysseldyke, J.E. & Algozzine, B. (1983). Where to begin in diagnosis of reading problems. *Topics in learning disabilities: Issues in reading diagnosis,* **2** (4), 60-69.

Index

Other ACER publications

Understanding Classroom Behaviour
MAURICE BALSON

Dr Balson's very successful book is now in its second edition — expanded to include two vital new chapters: 'Adolescence' and 'Mastery Learning'.

Otherwise, it's a total update of this excellent book for the classroom teacher, students of education, and parents.

The author knows all too well that today's schools and teachers face a much tougher task than ever before. But, he argues, the problems of classroom management will begin to fade away if schools promote good learning in all students.

Living in a Stepfamily
RUTH WEBBER

A unique video-based program for stepfamilies.

Betty Marshall, Marriage Guidance Council of NSW:
'Invaluable to all those working with stepfamilies and stepchildren.'

Gay Ochiltree, Australian Institute of Family Studies, about the video:
'Excellent for stimulating discussion about stepfamily issues, but equally useful for human relations education.'